MECHANICS OF
SMALL ENGINES

HENRY ATKINSON · THIRD EDITION

MECHANICS OF

SMALL ENGINES

HENRY ATKINSON · THIRD EDITION

McGraw-Hill Ryerson Ltd.

Toronto   Montréal   New York   Auckland   Bogotá   Cairo   Guatemala
Hamburg   Johannesburg   Lisbon   London   Madrid   Mexico   New Delhi
Panama   Paris   San Juan   São Paulo   Singapore   Sydney   Tokyo

Mechanics of Small Engines, Third Edition

Copyright © McGraw-Hill Ryerson Limited, 1986
Copyright © McGraw-Hill Ryerson Limited, 1978
Copyright © McGraw-Hill Company of Canada Limited, 1967

ISBN 0-07-548870-1

1 2 3 4 5 6 7 8 9 0   BP   5 4 3 2 1 0 9 8 7 6

Printed and bound in Canada

Cover design and photograph by Dave Hader

Canadian Cataloguing in Publication Data

Atkinson, Henry, date
  Mechanics of Small Engines

''SI Metric''
Includes index
ISBN 0-07-548870-1

1. Internal combustion engines.   I. Title

TJ785.A82   1985   621.43′4   C85-099379-2

CONTENTS

ACKNOWLEDGEMENTS

The author has received willing assistance from many individuals and organizations in the small engine field while preparing the material for this book. He gratefully acknowledges his indebtedness and sincerely thanks all who took the time to share their knowledge and resources. Special thanks to:

Snap-On Tools of Canada Ltd., London, Ont.

Outboard Marine of Canada Ltd., Peterborough, Ont.

Jos. St. Mars Eastern Ltd., Montreal, P.Q., and
Toronto, Ont.

Briggs and Stratton Engines Ltd., Milwaukee, Wisconsin,
U.S.A.

Mr. Charles Fowlie of Charles Fowlie and Sons Ltd.,
Tillsonburg, Ont.

Mr. Ben Johnson of B.F. Johnson Auto Electric Ltd.,
Tillsonburg, Ont.

Mr. George Hall of Hall's Recreation and Landscaping
Equipment Centre, Tillsonburg, Ont.

Mr. Art Williams of Art Williams Cycle Ltd., Tillsonburg, Ont.

Champion Spark Plug Co. of Canada, Ltd., Windsor, Ont.

H.F. Atkinson

PREFACE

This text is written and illustrated for use by the beginning student in small engine mechanics. Theory of operation is stressed, with a lesser emphasis on repair procedure.

The format of the third edition follows through from the second edition, providing the student with a meaningful, easy-to-comprehend learning resource. Each chapter begins with a list of new vocabulary, sentences in which the vocabulary is used, and a series of preview questions designed to call the reader's attention to important points. More preview questions can be found throughout the longer chapters. Theory consists of step-by-step, easy-to-comprehend descriptions written in simple, logical language, and clear, concise illustrations of examples, most of them in two colours. The one column page layout and accompanying colour margin aid greatly in the clear presentation of the material and by providing special safety, vocabulary, and service notes or illustrations alongside the procedure or operation to which they refer.

At this time, the SI metric system has not been fully adopted by North American small engine manufacturers. However, Asian and European manufactured imports are all built to metric standards. Because of this, the small engine mechanic must be able to work in both the old inch system and SI metric, and acquire separate sets of tools. This textbook edition presents important specifications in both systems for the student's convenience.

One of the problems of instruction in small engine mechanics is to provide the student with adequate practical experience. To this end most chapters are provided with a suggested list of related activities as well as pre-review questions. Although much of the practical work can be completed on shop engines, it is suggested that every effort be made to obtain actual "customer" repair jobs. Encourage the use of the trouble-shooting chapter.

H.F.A.

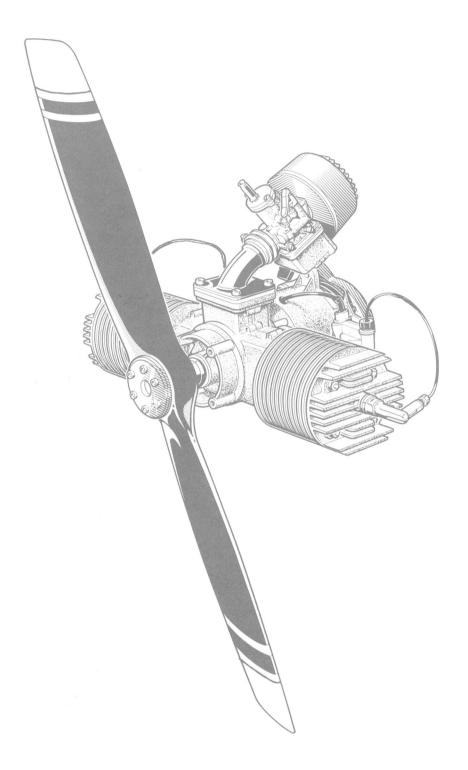

A two cylinder engine used in an ultralight aircraft

INTRODUCTION

The Small Engines Mechanic

So you have decided to study the operating principles and repair of small gasoline engines. You will find the engines in this category interesting and challenging in themselves, as well as in the many ways they are used. If you enjoy using your head and hands skilfully, and find it satisfying to locate an engine's need and repair it quickly, then perhaps this first course in small engines repair will be the beginning of your lifetime career.

With only this beginning course in engine repair, you should not expect to find a job as a fully-trained mechanic. What you learn from this book, your teacher, and the hands-on experience he or she can provide should make it possible for you to decide on your interest. You may wish to find a job in a small engines repair shop where you'll receive more training and experience. Many of the Canadian provinces have no regulations in place, as yet, to control the training and certification of small engines mechanics. This often includes the mechanics who repair motorcycles. The young person wishing to master the trade in these provinces must learn from experience while employed in an established repair shop. He or she may be able to get additional training by enrolling in night courses offered by local high schools or community colleges. In several provinces there are apprenticeship programs available that are regulated by the provincial governments.

*A small engine mechanic
at work on a four stroke
cycle engine powered
lawnmower*

CERTIFICATION

Ontario's Regulation 20, pertaining to the air-cooled and marine engine mechanic, outlines the apprenticeship and tradesman's route to qualification and certification in the trade. These regulations provide standard training for all small engine mechanics in the province except those who wish to qualify as motorcycle mechanics. Since motorcycles are considered motor vehicles, apprenticeship is compulsory and is controlled by separate regulations.

Learning to be a certified small engines mechanic begins by obtaining a job in an established small engines repair shop where the employer will agree to register you as an apprentice and provide the training described in the regulations. Although it is not compulsory for either you or your employer to enter into the apprenticeship program, you will find that many employers will not only insist on it, but will ask you to complete a small engines repair course at the community college level before beginning your apprenticeship. Of course it is to your advantage to become certified. You will find it much easier to find future employment when you can show your Certificate of Qualification.

In Ontario, the trade of air-cooled and marine engine mechanic is divided into four branches:

1. Small engine mechanic
2. Marine and small powered equipment mechanic
3. Small engine mechanic (construction)
4. Boat motor mechanic.

The apprenticeship training program for each of these branches is made up of a certain number of periods of work experience, plus related training periods at an approved college. Branches 1 and 2 require two periods of 2000 hours of work experience plus two 10-week training courses. Branch 3 also requires two 2000-hour work periods but only one 8-week related training course, and Branch 4 requires four 1800-hour periods of work experience plus two 10-week courses. The apprentice must pass practical and written examinations at the end of the training courses in order to earn certification.

Briefly, a small engine mechanic, for example, would be able to repair small air-cooled gasoline engines used to power such machines as snowblowers, lawnmowers, chainsaws, portable pumps and generators, outboard motors and snowmobiles. The mechanic should be able to locate causes of trouble and, using hand or power tools and instruments, replace, repair or recondition parts. The mechanic should also be able to clean, overhaul, repair or adjust carburetor and fuel systems, coil and magneto systems, electrical systems, power trains and asso-

*A self-propelled lawnmower
powered by a two stroke
cycle engine*

ciated components. The mechanic will also test performances of repaired or overhauled engines.

Regulation and certification for this trade is not uniform across Canada. For example, there is interest in Alberta in regulating motorcycle mechanics; however, the small engine mechanics trade is not likely to be regulated in the near future. No certificates are issued. Manitoba does not formally recognize the trade either, but small engine mechanics is one of several trades being considered for regulation and certification. There is regulation in Newfoundland and Labrador, though. In this province, a person entering the apprenticeship program to be a certified Small Equipment Mechanic must first find a job and then apply for apprenticeship to the Provincial Department of Labour and Manpower. If accepted, the apprentice then enters into a Contract of Apprenticeship with his or her employer. The period of apprenticeship is three years and includes attendance in classroom instruction as directed by the Manpower Training Division. Every apprentice must pass trade tests and examinations before receiving a certificate of qualification.

In New Brunswick, the Industrial Training and Certification Act provides for a voluntary four-year apprenticeship plan ending with a written examination. A mark of 65 per cent or better is considered a pass. The apprentice then receives a certificate of qualification in the Small Equipment Repair trade.

YOUR NEW TEXTBOOK

We have tried to make this textbook easy to read, and have used drawings and photographs wherever possible to help you to understand ideas quickly and easily. Colour has been used to direct your attention to the item being discussed, and the wide colour margin holds many tips, explanations and safety reminders that should help make the mechanic's job easier and safer.

There are millions of small engines in use in our country and each year many more are manufactured. As well, many thousands of small engines and machines powered by small engines are imported from other countries. Although Canada has adopted the SI metric system of measurement, our small engines manufacturers have not begun using it. This is mainly because their largest market is in the United States of America, where the old inch system of measurement is still the standard. On the other hand, engines imported from Japan and Europe have all been built to metric standards. This means that we have to be familiar with both systems and have the tools to fit them. Both systems are presented throughout this textbook.

Whatever your reason for studying small engines repair, this textbook and your teacher will help you to begin acquiring the knowledge and skills needed. The trade is always expanding; perhaps a new use for small engines, such as powering ultra-light aircraft, will capture your imagination and send you on the road to certification in this interesting field of technology.

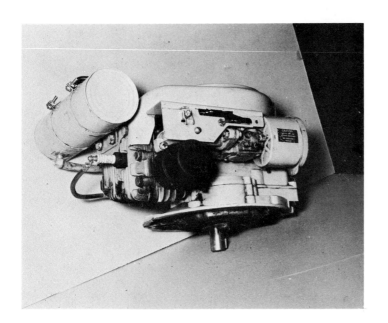

CHAPTER 1

THE SMALL ENGINE

Words to Learn

cylinder block	*camshaft*	*electrode*
crankcase	*timing gears*	*terminal*
cylinder head	*valve lifter*	*porcelain*
connecting rod	*valve*	*insulator*
piston	*magneto*	*carburetor*
crankshaft	*spark plug*	*flywheel*

How to Use These Words

1. The *cylinder head* is bolted to the *cylinder block* of many small engines.

2. The *crankshaft* is located in the *crankcase.*

3. The *piston* fits inside the cylinder.

4. The *connecting rod* joins the piston to the *crankshaft.*

5. A set of *timing gears* is used to make the *camshaft* turn half as fast as the *crankshaft.*

6. The intake and exhaust *valves* are opened by *valve lifters* that rest on the cams of the *camshaft.*

7. A *magneto* and *spark plug* make up the electrical system of a small engine.

8. When electricity jumps between the two spark plug *electrodes*, a spark occurs.

9. A thick wire connects the coil to the spark plug *terminal.*

5

10. *Porcelain* does not conduct electricity, so it is a good electrical *insulator.*

11. A *carburetor* mixes fuel and air in correct amounts.

12. The *flywheel* is fastened to one end of the *crankshaft.*

Look for Answers to These Questions:

1. What type of seals are used between a piston and its cylinder walls?

2. What type of small engine often has the cylinder head and upper cylinder block cast in one piece?

3. What type of valves are used in small four stroke cycle engines?

4. How is the up and down motion of the piston made to revolve the crankshaft?

5. What causes the camshaft to revolve?

6. How does a camshaft open the valves?

7. What causes the valves to close tightly?

8. What does the magneto do to make an engine run?

9. What two jobs does the carburetor perform for an engine?

10. What job does the spark plug do for an engine?

INTRODUCTION

Small engines, like automobile engines, must have regular care if they are to remain in good operating condition. Most car owners carefully follow the maker's suggestions for the proper care of their cars. They do this by seeing that the oil is changed at the proper time and that greasing and tune-ups are carried out regularly. Yet, the same owners often forget that the engines of their lawnmowers or outboards need the *same* care if they are to give them long and reliable service. Any engine will reward its owner with long and trouble-free service if its needs are cared for regularly. Service advice can be found in the operator's manual that the manufacturer gives out with each engine sold.

It is also possible to get very complete service manuals at low cost from the manufacturers of small engines. A small-engine mechanic should buy the service manuals for the types of engines he or she is most likely to be servicing.

There are two basic types of small engines. One is the simple two stroke cycle engine with very few moving parts. The other

Be careful: Do not run engines in a closed workshop. Exhaust fumes contain carbon monoxide gas. You can't see it, smell it, or taste it, but it can kill you.

type is the more complicated four stroke cycle engine with more moving parts and a smoother delivery of power. Both kinds of engines are used on gasoline-powered lawnmowers, outboard motors for small boats, and for many other units such as portable pumps and chain saws. Many air compressors for paint spraying outfits and rotary trowels to smooth concrete floors are also operated by small engines.

Be careful: Protect your hearing. Wear ear plugs or muffs when working in a noisy shop or near loud engine exhaust.

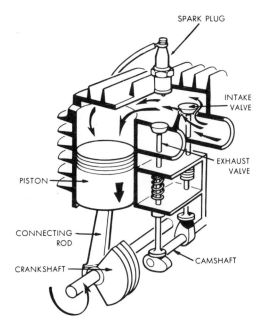

Four stroke cycle engine, cutaway drawing

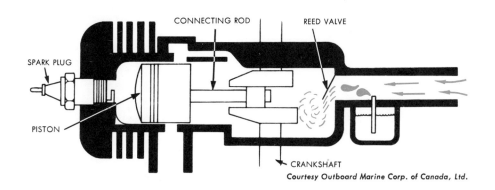

Courtesy Outboard Marine Corp. of Canada, Ltd.

Two stroke cycle engine, cutaway drawing

The Parts of the Engine

THE CYLINDER BLOCK

Cylinder block: the large, main part of any engine.

The cylinder block is the basic part of an engine. All other parts either fasten to it or are fastened inside it. The shape is often complicated, and the block is cast in a mould to obtain the necessary shape. Small engine blocks are sometimes made from cast iron, but most are cast from aluminum or other light metals.

THE CYLINDER

The cylinder is the name given to the large hole bored in the block. This hole receives the piston, which slides up and down in the cylinder bore after it has been smoothed and polished inside. The cylinder is not a separate part of the engine but it is important to the operation of the engine.

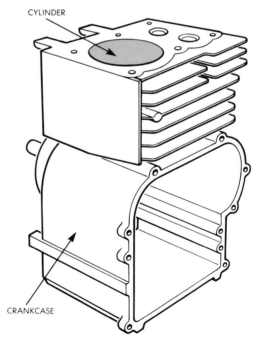

Cylinder and crankcase

THE CRANKCASE

Crankcase: the part of the cylinder block where the crankshaft revolves.

The crankcase is the lower part of the cylinder block, in which the crankshaft revolves. Some small engines have separate crankcase sections .These sections bolt to the cylinder block.

THE CYLINDER HEAD

Cylinder head: a metal cover bolted to the top of the cylinder block.

The cylinder head is a piece of metal shaped and bolted to the top of the cylinder block to cover the cylinder. It usually has a threaded hole for the spark plug and is hollowed out on the underside to form a combustion chamber. Sometimes, the cylinder head is cast with cooling fins attached, so that the air passing over the fins keeps the cylinder head cool. On small two stroke cycle engines, the cylinder head is often cast as one piece with the cylinder block.

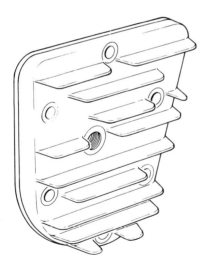

Cylinder head

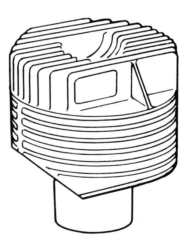

A one-piece cylinder head and upper cylinder block

Connecting rod: the connecting rod connects the piston to the crankshaft.

THE CONNECTING ROD

The connecting rod joins the piston to the crankshaft. One end of the rod is connected to the inside of the piston by means of a piston pin. The piston pin passes through both the piston and the top of the rod. The lower end of the connecting rod has a removable cap so the rod can be fastened to the crankshaft.

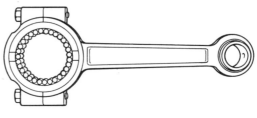

Connecting rod

THE PISTON

Piston: a round cylindrical piece of metal which fits in the cylinder of the engine block and moves up and down.

The piston is a cast piece of steel or aluminum made to fit very exactly into the cylinder. The piston has two or more steel piston rings around it to provide a seal between the piston and the cylinder walls. The piston moves up and down in the cylinder and is forced down in the cylinder by the pressure made by burning fuel.

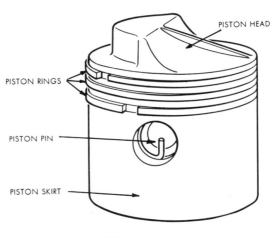

The piston

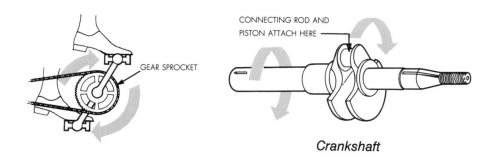

Crankshaft

THE CRANKSHAFT

Crankshaft: the rotating, main shaft in an engine. The pistons make it rotate.

The crankshaft changes the up and down motion of the piston and connecting rod to rotating motion, just as pedals allow a rider to propel a bicycle by changing the up and down motion of the rider's legs to the circular motion of the pedals and the chain sprocket. The bicycle rider's legs power the chain sprocket like the piston and connecting rod power the crankshaft.

THE CAMSHAFT

Camshaft: the shaft in an engine which pushes open the intake and exhaust valves.

The camshaft has two lobes, or cams, for each cylinder of the engine. Cams are off-centre lobes which open the intake and exhaust valves one after the other. The camshaft is driven by the crankshaft. The crankshaft has a small gear on one end which connects to a large gear on the end of the camshaft. As the crankshaft rotates, its gear turns the gear on the camshaft and causes it to rotate, too. These gears are called valve timing gears. Some engines use a chain and sprockets instead of gears. The chain is called a valve timing chain.

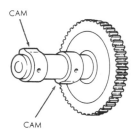

Camshaft

Timing gears: gears used to turn the camshaft and open and close the valves at the right time.

THE TIMING GEARS

The timing gears control the opening and closing of the valves so that each valve operates at the right time. The gear on the camshaft has twice as many teeth as the crankshaft gear; there-fore, the camshaft turns half as fast as the crankshaft.

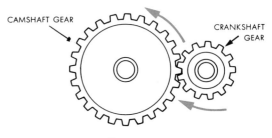

CAMSHAFT GEAR

CRANKSHAFT GEAR

Timing gears

THE VALVES

Valve: a device used to control the flow of air, gas, or liquid through a hole.

The valves are mushroom shaped, with long stems. They are made of steel. The intake valve, when open, allows fuel to enter the cylinder. The exhaust valve, when open, allows burnt gases to escape. When both valves are closed, nothing can get in or out of the cylinder.

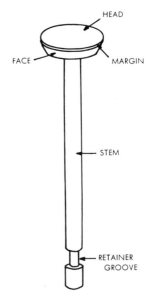

HEAD

FACE

MARGIN

STEM

RETAINER GROOVE

Poppet valve

THE VALVE LIFTERS

Each valve lifter rests on a cam on the camshaft and presses on the end of the valve stem to lift and open each of the valves at the right time.

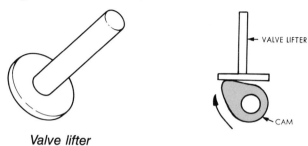

Valve lifter

THE VALVE SPRINGS

The valve springs are always pushing down on the valve stems, keeping the valves in the closed position, until a valve lifter pushes them open. For this reason, each valve closes tightly as soon as the highest point on the cam passes and the lifter releases pressure on the valve stem.

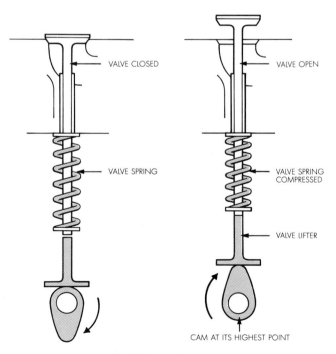

Valve springs

Valve lifters: small rods with one flat end. Valve lifters push valves open.

Spark plug: a device designed to make a powerful spark jump across a small gap in order to ignite fuel.

Electrodes: two wire-like parts of a spark plug that extend into the cylinder to provide a gap for an electric spark.

Porcelain: a hard, brittle material like china. Its surface is usually smooth and white.

Insulator: a substance which does not conduct electricity. Insulators are used to keep electricity from escaping from a line, and to shield other parts from electrical shock or current.

Terminal: a name given to all points in electrical devices where wires may be connected.

THE SPARK PLUG

The spark plug screws into a hole in the cylinder head. It is designed to provide a gap for an electric spark to jump between two pieces of steel, called electrodes. The threaded shell part of the plug is steel and the upper part is made from a material called porcelain, which is like the material used to make china plates and cups. Porcelain does not conduct electricity, so it is used as an electrical insulator. The lower electrode is fastened to the threaded part of the plug. The centre electrode passes through the porcelain and has a threaded end at the top. A round nut screws onto this threaded end to form a wire terminal. A heavy wire that comes from the magneto is pushed onto this round nut.

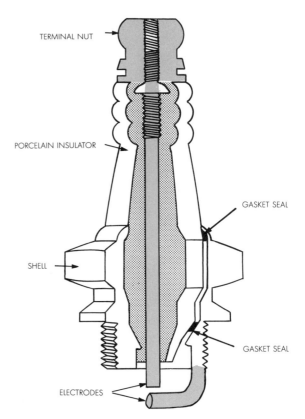

TERMINAL NUT

PORCELAIN INSULATOR

GASKET SEAL

SHELL

GASKET SEAL

ELECTRODES

Cutaway drawing of a spark plug

THE CARBURETOR

Carburetor: carburetors are used on gasoline engines to mix fuel and air in the right amounts.

The carburetor is a mixing place for fuel and air. The carburetor breaks up the fuel into a fine spray and mixes it with the right amount of air to make a mixture which will burn properly in the cylinder. The carburetor controls the crankshaft speed by the amount of fuel/air mixture it allows into the cylinder.

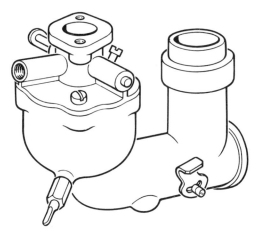

Carburetor

THE MAGNETO

Magneto: a device used to make an electric spark to ignite the fuel in the cylinder.

The magneto is made up of many smaller parts. We will look at it more closely in another chapter. All the parts of the magneto work together to make an electrical spark between the two points of the spark plug. The magneto makes the spark at the right time to ignite the fuel, which has just been sucked into the cylinder and compressed.

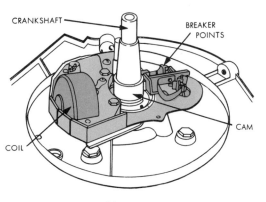

Magneto

Flywheel: a wheel that attaches to the crankshaft. It is used to help start the engine and keep it running smoothly.

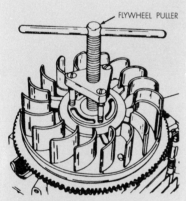

FLYWHEEL PULLER

Courtesy Tecumseh Products Canada, Ltd.

Using a flywheel puller to remove a flywheel

THE FLYWHEEL

The flywheel is a heavy, round metal casting that, on many engines, must do three or four jobs. It is fastened to one end of the crankshaft where its heavy mass helps make the crankshaft turn around evenly and smoothly between power strokes. The fins on the flywheel make it work like a fan to blow cooling air past the cylinder head and block. When a magnet is cast into the rim of the flywheel, it becomes part of the magneto. Whatever type of cranking device is used to start an engine, the flywheel is part of it. Sometimes the starter is only a rope wound around a pulley on the flywheel. Sometimes it is a heavy spring that may be wound tight and released to engage the flywheel. Many small engines today have electric starters. Electric starter motors crank an engine by spinning the flywheel.

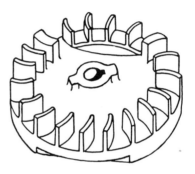

Flywheel

Things to Do

1. Use a cutaway drawing of a small engine to locate the parts listed and described in this chapter.

2. Compare the parts of a four stroke engine to those of a two stroke engine.

3. Make a list of as many uses for small engines as you can find.

4. Study the Words to Learn section and then write a list of parts of a four stroke engine.

5. Make a list of the parts of a two stroke engine.

6. Make a drawing of a piston and its connecting rod. Label the drawing.

7. Make a drawing of a crankshaft with timing gear at one end and a flywheel at the other end.

CHAPTER 2

AN ENGINE MECHANIC'S HAND TOOLS

Watch for These Words

swivel   gauge
ratchet   hone
extension   torque
universal   warp

How to Use These Words

1. A hinge joint in a wrench handle allows it to *swivel.*

2. A *ratchet* allows a wrench to turn a nut in only one direction, without having to turn the wrench handle completely around.

3. An *extension* will give a socket wrench more reach.

4. A *universal* joint allows torque to pass from one shaft to another shaft, even if the two shafts meet at an angle.

5. A *gauge* is an accurate measuring tool.

6. Fine grit stones are used in a cylinder *hone.*

7. A *torque* wrench measures the tightness of nuts and bolts.

8. You may *warp* a cylinder head by careless tightening of the head bolts.

A mechanic depends on knowledge and hand tools to make a living. Each repair job can be done quickly and safely if all the necessary tools are available and if they are clean and in good shape. A mechanic knows that when a tool is used properly, for the job for which it was made, it will serve him or her for many years.

This chapter shows you the hand tools most commonly used by small engine mechanics. Many other hand tools and power tools are available. These can be bought and added to the mechanic's collection as they are needed.

Wrenches

Find the Answers to These Questions

1. Why are the openings in open end wrenches set on an angle?
2. Which style of wrench opening is least likely to slip off a tight fastener?
3. What style of wrench is sized by its length?
4. List three standard square drive sizes used in socket wrench sets.
5. Why are socket wrenches made in both standard and deep styles?
6. When is it best to use a six point socket?
7. List the names of four styles of socket wrench handles.
8. Why is a torque wrench so important to a good mechanic?

Wrenches are made in a wide range of styles, lengths, and sizes. They can be bought one at a time or in sets and half sets. A half set has every other wrench. For example, if a set has ten wrenches, a half set would have numbers 2, 4, 6, 8 and 10 included.

OPEN END WRENCHES

Open end wrenches are made in SI metric sizes from 6 mm to 32 mm and inch system sizes from ¼ inch to 1⅝ inch. The size is the distance across the end opening. Each wrench has openings for two sizes of bolt head. Some examples of size pairs are: 6 mm and 7 mm, 8 mm and 9 mm, 10 mm and 11 mm 12 mm and 14 mm, 13 mm and 15 mm.

The open ends are set on a slight angle to the handle so that the wrench can be used in places where there is little room to move it. If the wrench will not fit in one position turn it over, and try it in the other position.

Open end wrenches are used with both square and hexagon shaped nuts and bolts.

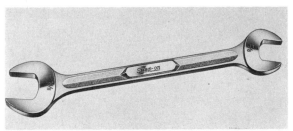

Courtesy Snap-On Tools of Canada Ltd.

Open end wrench

BOX END WRENCHES

Box end wrenches are available in SI metric sizes from 6 mm to 41 mm and in inch system sizes from ⅜ inch to 1⅝ inch. Like the open end style, each wrench fits two sizes. Box end wrenches fit only hexagon head bolts and nuts. They do not tend to slip off.

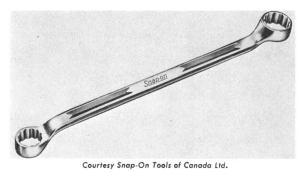

Courtesy Snap-On Tools of Canada Ltd.

Box end wrench

Safety Note: It is best to pull on a wrench rather than to push it. You can hurt yourself if the wrench slips off the nut or bolt.

COMBINATION WRENCHES

Combination wrenches have one box end and one open end. They are made in all of the standard metric sizes. Both ends of each wrench are the same size. A complete set of combination wrenches has twice the number of wrenches as either the box end or open end styles.

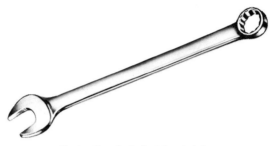

Courtesy Snap-On Tools of Canada Ltd.

Combination wrench

ADJUSTABLE WRENCHES

Adjustable wrenches are sized by the length of the wrench. At the present time, they are made only in inch sizes. A set of three wrenches, 6 in., 8 in. and 10 in., would be most useful to a small engines mechanic. The jaw opening is adjusted by turning a worm gear. This gear should click into each position to keep the opening from changing during use. Adjustable wrenches do not fit as well as other styles, so they should only be used when another wrench is not available.

Courtesy Snap-On Tools of Canada Ltd.

Adjustable wrench

SOCKET WRENCHES

Socket wrenches are usually sold in sets. These sets include a range of socket sizes and a variety of handles that can be used with each socket. The handles and sockets are made in seven standard drive sizes. The smaller sizes best suit the work done by a mechanic of small engines. These are the ¼ in. Midget, ⅜ in. Ferret, and ½ in. Standard square drive sizes. The manufacturers are continuing to use the inch size names for the square drive so that mechanics can buy SI metric sockets to fit their old handles. Soon they may use metric names, even though the square drives will still be designed in inches. These metric names will probably be 6.3 mm, 9.5 mm, and 12.7 mm.

MIDGET
¼ IN. SQ. DRIVE

FERRET
⅜ IN. SQ. DRIVE

STANDARD
½ IN. SQ. DRIVE

Drive sizes

Any socket set can be bought in standard or deep styles, with either six or twelve point openings. Deep sockets are useful when removing or replacing nuts on bolts that have extra thread length. They will reach into many areas where standard sockets cannot be used.

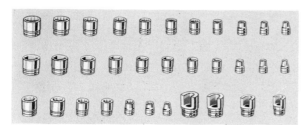

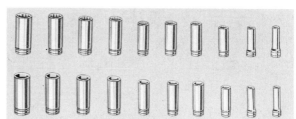

Courtesy Snap-On Tools of Canada Ltd.

Standard length sockets

Deep sockets

Six point sockets fit hexagon headed fasteners snugly. There is very little chance that the wrench will slip off, or tear the corners off of the bolt head.

Twelve point sockets allow the wrench handle to be placed in twice as many positions when there is little room to move it. It is best to use a six point socket to remove a very tight nut or bolt. The small points of a twelve point socket might tear the corners off a really tight fastener.

12 POINT SOCKET   6 POINT SOCKET

Twelve point and six point sockets

A set of Midget square drive sockets will fit nut and bolt sizes from 4 mm to 14 mm ($\frac{1}{8}$ inch to $\frac{9}{16}$ inch). Ferret square drive sockets will fit sizes from 6 mm to 26 mm ($\frac{1}{4}$ inch to $\frac{7}{8}$ inch). Standard square drive sockets are made in all sizes from 10 mm to 36 mm ($\frac{3}{8}$ inch to $1\frac{5}{16}$ inch).

SOCKET DRIVE HANDLES

The tee handle has a drive unit that may be slid along the cross bar to any position.

Tee handle

Swivel: to swing or turn on a hinge pin.

The swivel bar has a hinged drive end that allows the wrench to be pulled through a half turn and then swung over for the next pull.

Swivel bar

Ratchet: a mechanical device that allows free motion in only one direction.

A ratchet handle is used whenever movement of the wrench is limited. The ratchet can be used in both left and right directions for either tightening or loosening operations.

Courtesy Snap-On Tools of Canada Ltd.

Ratchet handle

A speeder is used for rapid driving or removal of long bolts and screws. With the swivel end, it can be used like a swivel bar.

Courtesy Snap-On Tools of Canada Ltd.

Speeder

TORQUE WRENCHES

Torque: the amount of turning force applied to or by a shaft.

Warp: to bend or twist out of shape.

Be careful: Torque wrenches should be stored separate from other wrenches to keep them accurate and free from damage.

A torque wrench is an expensive but necessary part of every tool kit. It is used to tighten nuts and bolts to accurate degrees of torque (amount of twist force) so that no bolt will be tightened more or less than the others. This prevents warping of machine parts.

Torque wrenches are available to fit all of the square drive sockets. Torque is measured in newton metres. The small engines mechanic would have use for the 60 N·m and 250 N·m torque wrench sizes. Not all torque wrenches have a dial to measure the torque applied; some can be preset to click when the correct amount of tightness is reached. Inch system torque wrenches measure inch-pounds or foot-pounds of torque.

Courtesy Snap-On Tools of Canada Ltd.

Torque wrench

Extension: a part that adds length.

Universal: A double-hinged connector used to apply torque through an angle.

SOCKET EXTENSIONS

Extensions are made in many lengths, in all drive sizes. They make it possible to reach into difficult locations.

Courtesy Snap-On Tools of Canada Ltd.

Extensions

UNIVERSAL JOINT

A universal joint is useful where space is limited or where something prevents normal wrench motion. It allows torque to be applied through an angle.

Courtesy Snap-On Tools of Canada Ltd.

Universal joint

CHAIN WRENCH

Chain wrenches are made in several styles and sizes. They may be used to hold or turn round shafts. The small engines mechanic will often use a chain wrench to hold the flywheel while removing or replacing the flywheel nut.

Courtesy Snap-On Tools of Canada Ltd.

Chain wrench

Pliers, Screwdrivers and Special Tools

Find the Answers to These Questions

1. Name four styles of gripping pliers.
2. What style of pliers is designed so that its jaws tend to stay parallel?
3. Name the style of screwdriver used with these slot patterns: A, B, C.

Slot patterns

4. Name five styles of punches used by mechanics.
5. When is a cold chisel not in safe condition for use?
6. In which direction should the teeth of a hacksaw point?
7. Describe the type of work each of the following tools is designed to do:
   - (a) cylinder hone
   - (b) piston ring compressor
   - (c) cylinder ridge cutter
   - (d) gear puller
   - (e) thickness gauge
8. What is a micrometer?

PLIERS

Pliers are made in the standard styles shown here, and in many other styles for special jobs. The jaws of gripping pliers have sharp grooves to hold round objects. These grooves will damage any surface, so do not use pliers on finished or machined parts. Pliers should never be used to remove or install nuts and bolts. The shape of the nut or bolt head would be badly damaged, and no wrench would fit it afterwards.

Be careful: Loose clothing, long hair, jewelry, hands, arms, and feet can easily get caught in spinning flywheels, blades, gears chains, and belts.

Caution: Remember to clean each tool after use and replace it in its proper position in your tool box or cabinet.

Slip joint pliers have four spacer holes to allow quick adjustment of the jaw opening.

Courtesy Snap-On Tools of Canada Ltd.

Slip joint pliers

Groove joint pliers have a raised, curved section on one handle that slides into any one of five recessed grooves in the other handle, to provide the desired jaw opening. The jaws tend to remain parallel to each other in any position.

Courtesy Snap-On Tools of Canada Ltd.

Groove joint pliers

Needle nose pliers are designed to grip small objects, reach into deep locations, and coil or loop wire.

Courtesy Snap-On Tools of Canada Ltd.

Needle nose pliers

Diagonal cutting pliers are used for cutting wire. They are made in several standard lengths.

Courtesy Snap-On Tools of Canada Ltd.

Diagonal cutting pliers

Vise grip pliers have double action locking jaws. They can be used as pliers, a vise, or a clamp.

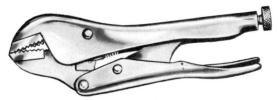

Courtesy Snap-On Tools of Canada Ltd.

Vise grip pliers

SCREWDRIVERS

Screwdrivers are made to drive and remove wood and machine screws. They should never be used as pry bars or levers. Do not use a screwdriver that has a badly worn tip. It will damage the screw heads. Grind the tip back to its right shape if possible, or replace it with a new screwdriver.

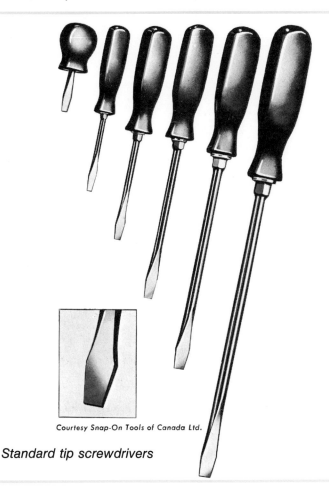

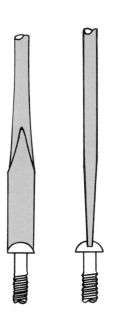

THIS IS THE WAY
A STANDARD TIP
SCREWDRIVER SHOULD FIT.

Courtesy Snap-On Tools of Canada Ltd.

Standard tip screwdrivers

Standard tip screwdrivers are available in many blade lengths and widths to fit all standard slotted screws. The correct tip size to use is the one that exactly fits the length and width of the screw slot. Worn tips can be carefully reground to the original shape.

Phillips screwdrivers are made in many lengths, with tips to fit Phillips slotted screws. Tips are sized No. 1, No. 2, No. 3 and No. 4 in a set.

Be careful: Wear safety glasses to protect your eyes while using grinders, chisels, hammers, and air hoses.

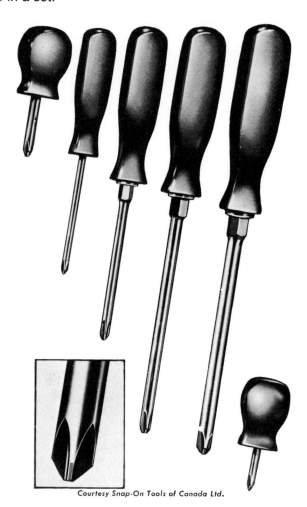

Courtesy Snap-On Tools of Canada Ltd.

Phillips screwdrivers

Robertson screwdrivers are made in five sizes. They have colour coded handles. The green-handled driver fits numbers 5, 6 and 7 Robertson square slotted screws. The red-handled driver fits numbers 8 and 9, and the black-handled driver fits numbers 12 and 14 screws. These are the sizes most often used.

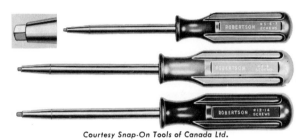

Courtesy Snap-On Tools of Canada Ltd.

Robertson screwdrivers

PUNCHES

The photographs show the types of punches that would be most useful in small engine repair work. Each style of punch is made in several tip sizes. The mechanic should have three or four of the smaller sizes of each, from 2 mm to 6 mm.

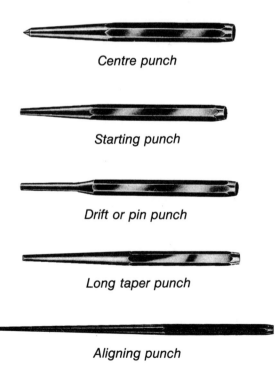

Centre punch

Starting punch

Drift or pin punch

Long taper punch

Aligning punch

COLD CHISELS

Two or three sizes of cold chisels should be included in a mechanic's tool box. A chisel is not used often, but sometimes is the only tool that can remove a badly rusted nut or bolt.

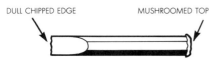

DULL CHIPPED EDGE   MUSHROOMED TOP

A COLD CHISEL THAT IS NOT SAFE TO USE

Cold chisel

HACKSAWS

Hacksaws are made in solid or adjustable frame styles. The adjustable frame saws can be lengthened or shortened to fit any standard length blade.

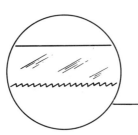

HACKSAW BLADE ENLARGED

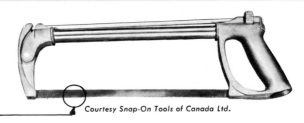

Courtesy Snap-On Tools of Canada Ltd.

Hacksaw

A hacksaw cuts on the forward stroke, so be sure to install the blade with the teeth pointing away from the handle.

HAMMERS

Only two types of hammers are needed for small engine work. These are the ball peen hammer in two head masses, and the soft face hammer with replaceable plastic tips.

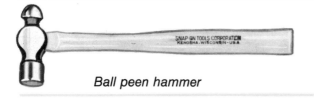

Ball peen hammer

Courtesy Snap-On Tools of Canada Ltd.

Soft face hammer

VALVE SPRING COMPRESSORS

These tools make valve removal a simple job. Two available styles are shown. Each style has a set of jaw sizes to fit most valve springs.

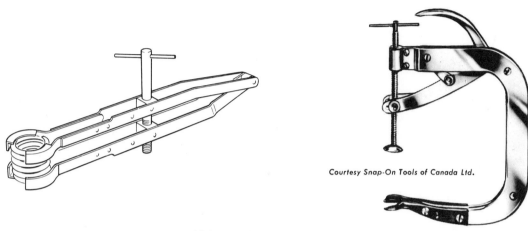

Courtesy Snap-On Tools of Canada Ltd.

Valve spring compressors

PISTON RING COMPRESSOR

A piston ring compressor with a 35 mm to 75 mm (1½ inch to 3 inch) capacity will fit all small engine pistons. The compressor is made of spring steel. It has a band which wraps around the piston to push the rings into their grooves. This allows the piston to be installed in the cylinder. A key-operated friction clutch tightens or loosens the band.

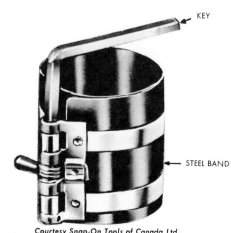

KEY

STEEL BAND

Piston ring compressor

Courtesy Snap-On Tools of Canada Ltd.

GEAR PULLER

A small two- or three-jawed puller finds many uses in small engine repair work. It may be used when removing pulleys, bearings and gears from their shafts. Many flywheels have holes drilled near the hub so that a puller may be used.

Gear puller

Hone: a tool used to finish cylinders and drilled holes to size.

CYLINDER HONE

When new piston rings are being installed, this tool is often used to roughen the cylinder walls for faster seating of the rings. It is also used to hone badly worn cylinders oversize. A new oversize piston must then be installed. The hone must be driven by a drill or drill press.

Be extra careful when using a hone in aluminum cylinders. A few sharp pieces of stone might become stuck in the cylinder wall. If that happened, new piston rings would soon get badly damaged.

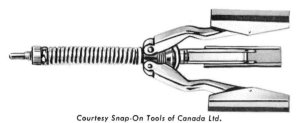

Courtesy Snap-On Tools of Canada Ltd.

Cylinder hone

CYLINDER RIDGE CUTTER

This tool is used to remove the slight ridge that is often left around the top of the cylinder where the piston rings do not travel. A new piston ring striking this ridge would damage both itself and the piston.

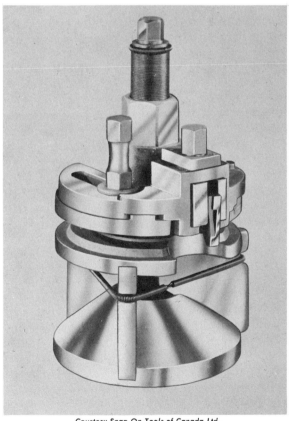

Courtesy Snap-On Tools of Canada Ltd.

Cylinder ridge cutter

Gauge: a tool for measuring or checking measurement.

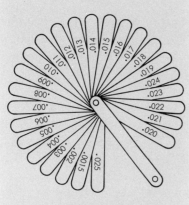

Inch system thickness gauge

Be careful: When a tool shows signs of wear, repair or replace it immediately so it can be used safely the next time you need it.

THICKNESS GAUGE

A thickness gauge is used to measure clearances between parts, such as piston ring groove clearances and ignition point gaps. A set of gauges is shown here. The number on each gauge gives its thickness in hundredths of a millimetre. For example, the 0.25 gauge is twenty-five hundredths of a millimetre thick. Inch system gauges measure in thousandths of an inch.

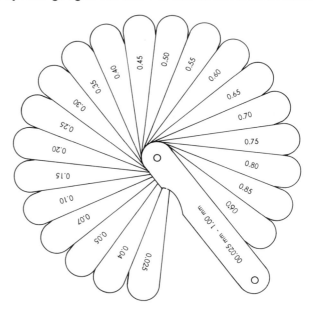

Thickness gauge

WIRE GAP GAUGE

A mechanic uses this tool to check and adjust the spark gap on spark plugs. The diameter of the wire is stamped on each gauge. A bending tool is provided for bending the side electrode of the spark plug.

Courtesy Snap-On Tools of Canada Ltd

Wire gap gauge

MICROMETERS

Micrometers are very accurate measuring tools. The micrometer you buy should measure in hundredths of a millimetre. More expensive micrometers can measure in thousandths of a millimetre. Inch system micrometers may measure in hundredths, thousandths, or ten thousandths of an inch.

Outside micrometers are used to measure the diameters of shafts and pistons.

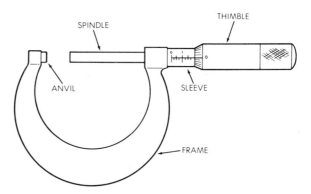

Outside micrometer

Inside micrometers are used to measure the inside diameters of cylinders and bearings.

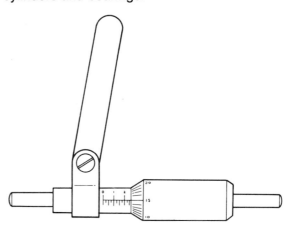

Inside micrometer

Since micrometers can measure so accurately, they can be used to detect the slightest wear on engine parts. If this wear is greater than the engine manufacturer specifies as a safe operating limit, the part must be replaced.

Micrometers should be stored in separate boxes made for them. Do not keep them in the tool box with your wrenches.

CHAPTER 3

FOUR STROKE CYCLE ENGINES

Watch for These Words

pilot	*peen*	*hone*
abrasive	*alloy*	*sprocket*
lapping	*combustion*	*intake manifold*
reamer	*corrosion*	*gaskets*

How to Use These Words

1. The *pilot* of the valve seat grinder fits into the valve guides of the engine.
2. Fine grinding *abrasive* is used when *lapping* valves and valve seats for a tight fit.
3. A *reamer* is used to make the hole through a valve guide the same size as the valve stem.
4. *Peen* the metal around a new valve seat insert in order to hold it in place.
5. An *alloy* is a metal made by carefully mixing two or more metals and special materials together.
6. The high temperatures and gases from fuel *combustion* can cause *corrosion* of valves and valve seats.
7. A *hone* is a tool used to smooth and straighten cylinder walls.
8. A *sprocket* is a type of gear made to fit the links of a chain.
9. The short pipe between the carburetor and cylinder on some engines is called the *intake manifold*.

36

10. *Gaskets* are made of flexible material to seal the joints between engine parts.

Find the Answers to These Questions

1. Name the four strokes that make up the four stroke operating cycle.
2. In which direction is the piston moving during each of the four strokes?
3. Describe the position of the intake and exhaust valves during each stroke.
4. What is the correct name for the type of valve used in four stroke engines?
5. Why is it important to replace each valve in its original position after reconditioning?
6. How does a worn valve affect the operation of the engine?
7. Name the part of the engine that opens the valves.
8. How would a weak or broken valve spring affect the operation of the engine?
9. List at least three flaws in a valve that show it should be replaced.
10. Why must there be a gap between the valve stem and the lifter?

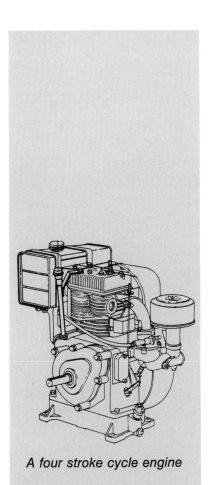

A four stroke cycle engine

Four Stroke Cycle Engine Operation

All gasoline engines must do four basic actions to operate properly. They must:

(a) suck in a mixture of fuel and air,

(b) squeeze the mixture into a small space,

(c) fire the mixture and use the force of the burning fuel to turn a crankshaft, and

(d) push the burned gases out of the cylinder into the air.

Some engines can complete these operations with only two strokes of the piston, up and down. Others need four strokes of the piston, up and down twice, to complete the cycle. In this chapter we will see how a four stroke cycle works.

THE INTAKE STROKE

With the exhaust valve closed and the intake valve open, the piston moves down in the cylinder as the engine crankshaft turns. This movement causes a fuel and air mixture to be sucked from the carburetor into the cylinder past the intake valve. The intake valve is held open by one of the cam lobes on the camshaft.

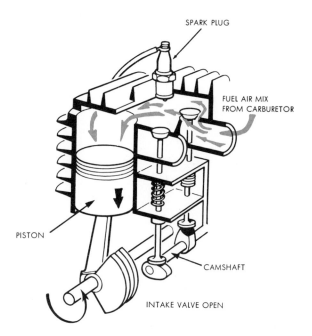

Single cylinder engine cutaway — intake stroke

A four stroke cycle engine with a horizontal crankshaft

THE COMPRESSION STROKE

When the piston reaches the bottom of the intake stroke, the camshaft allows the intake valve to close, the crankshaft continues to turn, and the piston moves upward on the compression stroke. The fuel mixture is trapped and squeezed into the small space between the top of the piston and the cylinder head. Squeezing gases into a small space is called compression.

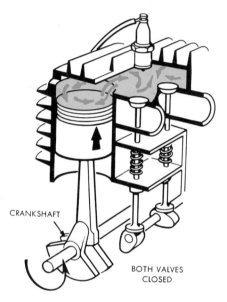

CRANKSHAFT

BOTH VALVES
CLOSED

*Single cylinder engine cutaway —
compression stroke*

*A four stroke cycle engine
with a vertical crankshaft*

THE POWER STROKE

As the piston nears the top point of its travel, called *top dead centre (TDC),* the ignition system is timed to cause a spark to jump across the gap between the electrode points of the spark plug. The fuel then begins to burn and the gases that form expand quickly in the tremendous heat. Pressure builds up and pushes outward on the cylinder walls, the cylinder head, and the top of the piston. The piston is the only part free to move, so it is pushed down in the cylinder, making the crankshaft turn around. The power that is created on this stroke must be great enough to keep the piston moving through the other three strokes of the operating cycle and do the work for which the engine was designed. The heavy flywheel helps to smooth out the surge of power and keep the crankshaft in motion.

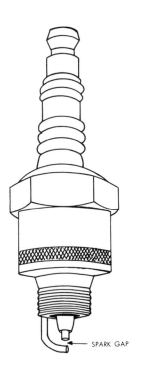

SPARK GAP

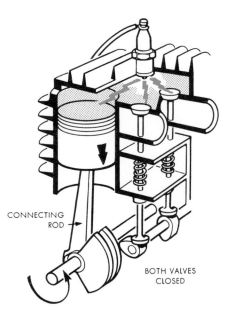

CONNECTING ROD

BOTH VALVES CLOSED

*Single cylinder engine cutaway —
power stroke*

THE EXHAUST STROKE

When the piston is moving downward at the end of the power stroke, the exhaust valve begins to open. It is fully opened by the time the *bottom dead centre (BDC)* position is reached. The upward travel of the piston on the exhaust stroke pushes the burned gases past the exhaust valve and out through the muffler.

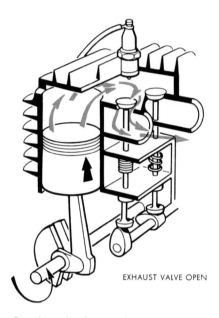

EXHAUST VALVE OPEN

*Single cylinder engine cutaway —
exhaust stroke*

After the exhaust stroke is completed, the whole cycle of operation starts again. The camshaft allows the exhaust valve to close, opens the intake valve, and the piston begins its downward travel on the intake stroke.

The operation of the four stroke cycle style of engine depends on the timing of its valves and their condition, on the piston rings, and on the cylinder walls. The remainder of this chapter deals with these parts in detail.

Valves

The valves are opened by the cam lobes on the revolving camshaft.

Lobe: a rounded, projecting part of a revolving shaft.

Look for Answers to These Questions

1. What is a valve seat insert?
2. How are valve seat inserts held in place?
3. Why is it important that the insert fit tightly in its mounting hole?
4. Why should the valve seat be no wider than 1.5 mm or $1/16$ inch?
5. What is valve overlap?
6. What is the purpose of valve overlap?
7. Name the two common types of camshaft drives.
8. How does a mechanic know whether he has replaced a camshaft in its correct position?
9. Why must the camshaft revolve at only half the speed of the crankshaft?
10. What causes the valves to close tightly against their seats?

Notice in the first drawings in this chapter that a single cylinder engine has two valves. This is the standard number per cylinder in almost all four stroke cycle engines, with the exception of some aircraft engines and racing car engines, which have four valves per cylinder.

Each valve is like an automatic gate or stopper, opening and closing passages leading to the cylinder. One closes off the passage from the carburetor to the cylinder and is called the intake valve. The other closes off the passage from the cylinder to the muffler and is called the exhaust valve.

Since this type of valve pops open and closed, it is known as a *poppet valve.* The camshaft is made so that its lobes push the valves open at the right time. Heavy coil springs hold the valves closed until the cam lobes push them open.

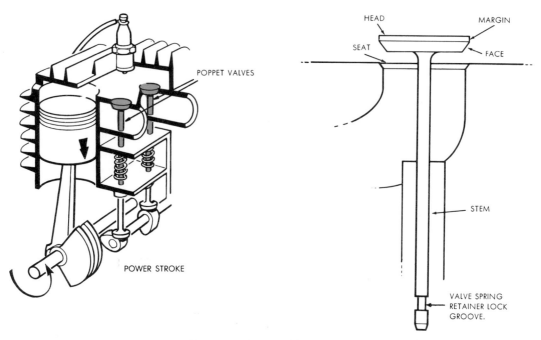

POPPET VALVES

POWER STROKE

HEAD

MARGIN

SEAT

FACE

STEM

VALVE SPRING
RETAINER LOCK
GROOVE.

Poppet valve and its parts

Combustion: what happens when fuel, such as gas, coal, or wood, starts to burn.

Corrosion: a chemical process which causes metal or other materials to be slowly eaten away.

The condition of the valves and valve seats has a great deal of control over cylinder compression and power output. Valves operate in very high temperatures inside the combustion chamber, and must maintain a tight seal when closed, whether the engine has just been started or has been running for a long period of time. Although both valves are subjected to the heat of combustion, the intake valve is partly cooled by each fresh charge of fuel entering the cylinder. The exhaust valve is usually made of a special steel that can resist heat and corrosion from the exhaust gases. It must never be exchanged with the intake valve.

The heat soaked up by the head of the valve must escape through the valve seat to the cylinder block. Then the heat must be taken away by the cooling system, as described in the chapter on cooling systems. Some of the heat travels down the stem of the valve and escapes through the valve guide. When a valve, valve seat, or valve guide becomes worn, heat cannot escape and the head of the valve burns or warps out of shape. A burned or warped valve can lower the compression of a cylinder so that it no longer operates.

VALVE GUIDES

The poppet valves must open and close hundreds of times every minute. Each time they must close tightly against the valve seats. Worn valve guides that allow the valve stem to wobble back and forth will cause one side of the valve to ride high on the seat. Compression pressure and power can then leak past the face of the valve.

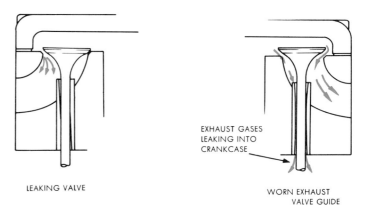

LEAKING VALVE

EXHAUST GASES
LEAKING INTO
CRANKCASE

WORN EXHAUST
VALVE GUIDE

Heat also cannot now escape from the valve head to the seat and cylinder block. Exhaust valves warp and burn very quickly in this condition.

Since valve guides extend into the crankcase, worn guides will allow lubricating oil to be sucked into the cylinder right past the stem of the intake valve, and also allow exhaust gases to be drawn into the crankcase past the exhaust valve. Oil burning, and carbon deposits in the oil are the results.

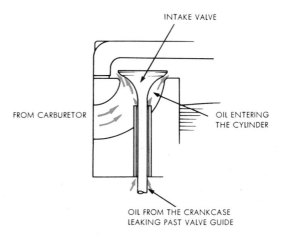

INTAKE VALVE

FROM CARBURETOR

OIL ENTERING
THE CYLINDER

OIL FROM THE CRANKCASE
LEAKING PAST VALVE GUIDE

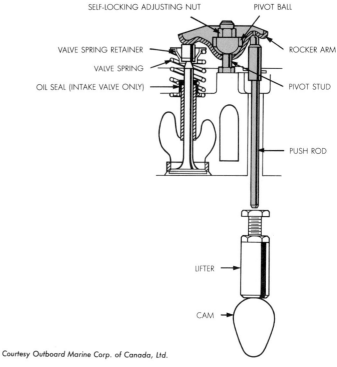

SELF-LOCKING ADJUSTING NUT

PIVOT BALL

VALVE SPRING RETAINER

ROCKER ARM

VALVE SPRING

OIL SEAL (INTAKE VALVE ONLY)

PIVOT STUD

PUSH ROD

LIFTER

CAM

Courtesy Outboard Marine Corp. of Canada, Ltd.

A push rod and rocker arm are needed to open valves in an overhead valve engine

Reamer: a tool used to make a hole larger. Reamers make very accurate holes. Reamers may be twisted by hand or by machine.

In some engines the valve guides are nothing more than holes drilled carefully through the crankcase. When these become worn, they can be reamed oversize with a special reamer, as shown below.

A valve guide bushing is then driven into the hole and reamed to fit the valve stem.

A reamer

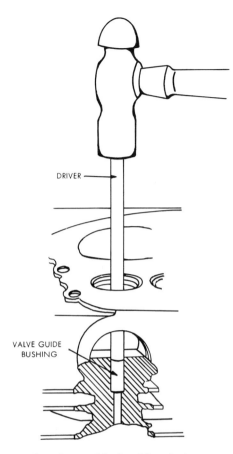

A valve guide bushing being driven in place

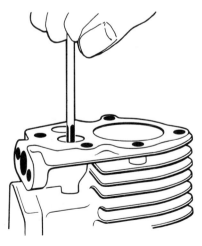

Reaming for a new valve guide

When the engine is equipped with removable valve guides, it is a simple job to press out the old guide and drive or press in a new one.

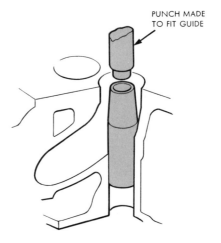

Fitting a new valve guide

It is then usually necessary to ream the new guide bushing so the valve stem will just fit into it. Check the repair manual for the correct stem to guide clearance.

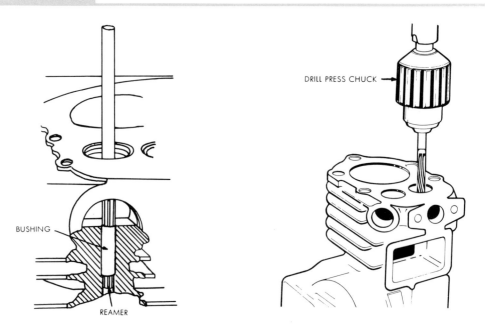

Reaming to fit valve stem

REMOVING VALVES

Gasket: a flat piece of material, usually rubber, paper, or asbestos, which is fitted between metal parts to keep fluids like oil from leaking out.

Be careful: Place all the engine parts in order on the bench as you remove them. This will make it easy to put the engine back together.

1. Remove the cylinder head and scrape off the old gasket. A putty knife is a good tool for this job, but remember to stuff a soft cloth into the cylinder to catch any dirt that falls in.

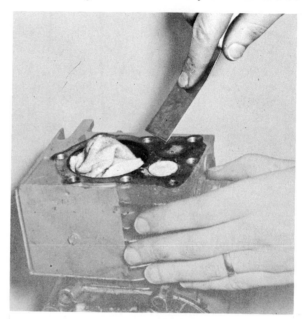

Scraping off old gasket

2. Remove the cover plate on the side of the cylinder block and use a valve spring compressor to lift the spring free of its retainer.

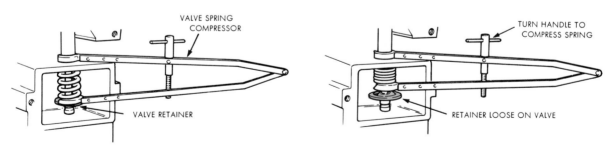

Lifting the spring free of its retainer

3. Use a pair of needle nose pliers to remove the valve spring retainer. The valve can now be lifted out of the cylinder block.

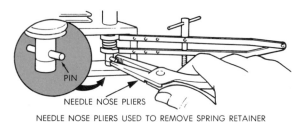

NEEDLE NOSE PLIERS USED TO REMOVE SPRING RETAINER

Removing the spring retainer

Intake manifold: the pipe used to bring the fuel-air mixture from the carburetor to the cylinder for combustion.

Note that some engines require the removal of other parts, such as the carburetor and intake manifold, before the cover plate can be removed. Reverse the steps to replace the valve.

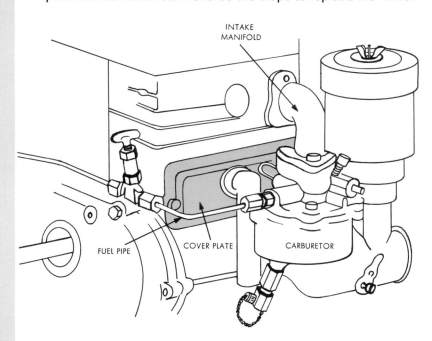

Breather vented through carburetor

The cover plate also serves as the crankcase breather location, and should be inspected to make sure the one way valve is working. The valve should allow air to escape when the engine's piston moves down in the cylinder, and then close to prevent air from entering on the up-stroke. This causes a partial vacuum in the crankcase to prevent oil from being forced out of the engine past the piston rings, oil seals and gaskets. Most modern engines have the breather connected to the carburetor after the air cleaner to prevent dirt from entering the crankcase.

RECONDITIONING VALVES

It is wise to carefully inspect each valve before any cleaning or grinding is attempted. If the valve head is burned or warped, the stem bent, the margin too thin, or the face worn too deeply, the valve should be thrown away and a new one installed.

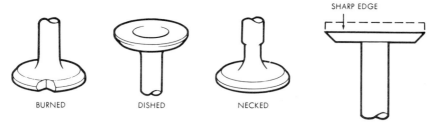

Valve conditions that cannot be fixed

Lapping: polishing, using an abrasive mounted on a special backing, such as brass, wool, leather, etc.

When lack of compression has been traced to leaking valves, and they show no serious damage, the valve faces will need grinding. This can be done only on a valve grinding machine, which can be adjusted to the exact angle of the face and will produce a finish that needs little or no lapping to the seat (wearing to a fine close fit).

Valve grinding machine in operation

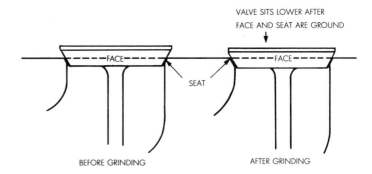

Since the grinding operation removes metal from the face, the valve will sit lower in its seat than before. Resurfacing the valve seat will add to this condition. It then becomes necessary to adjust the gap between the valve stem and the valve lifter.

Be careful: Is the valve margin going to be wide enough after grinding?

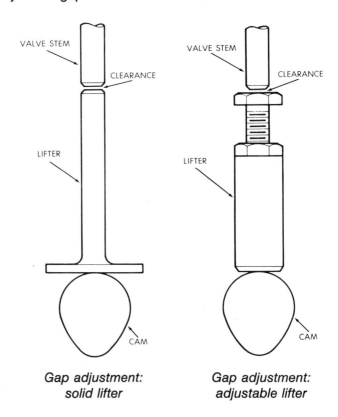

*Gap adjustment:
solid lifter*   *Gap adjustment:
adjustable lifter*

This clearance gap must be set according to the maker's suggestions, to allow the parts to expand when the engine gets hot while running.

Be careful: If you grind the valve stem too short, you must buy a new valve. Refer to the engine manual for the grinding allowance. The end of the stem has been hardened to resist wear.

If the gap were too small the valve would be lifted up off its seat when the valve and lifter expanded with the heat. Then the valve would burn and a lot of compression would be lost. Some engines have adjustable lifters, but most small engines have solid lifters that cannot be adjusted. In order to get the right gap with solid lifters, the tip of the valve stem must be ground off the correct amount, using the valve grinding machine. Take care when adjusting or grinding to arrive at a gap that is the same as the maker suggests. Check the clearance with a flat feeler gauge as shown.

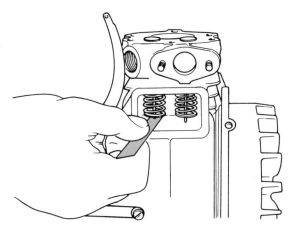

Using a thickness feeler gauge to check clearance between valve stem and lifter

VALVE SEAT RECONDITIONING

In cast iron engines, the valve seats are often machined directly on the edges of the intake and exhaust passages. Other engines, especially aluminum ones, use a steel insert.

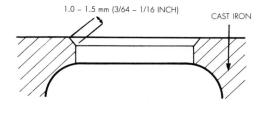

Valve seat machined on cast iron cylinder block

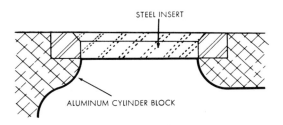

Steel valve insert in aluminum block

Pilot: a device which is used on valve seat cutters and grinders to guide and hold them in the correct position while cutting and grinding.

In either case, the seat should be ground or machined whenever the valve faces are reconditioned. Special cutters and grinders are used for this job. Steel seat inserts in aluminum engines can be removed and replaced with new seats when they are badly worn. The new seats must be ground to line up with the valve head. Valve seat cutters and grinders are equipped with several pilots to fit the valve guides of any engine. The pilot is the part that holds the tool in position.

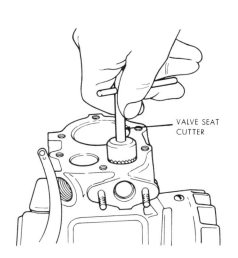

VALVE SEAT CUTTER

Valve seat cutter in operation

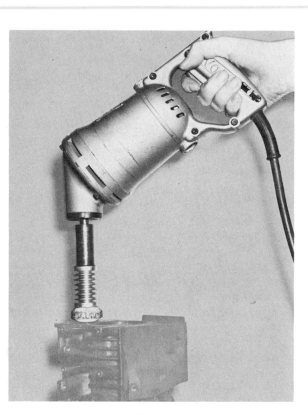

Grinding the valve seat

Peen: to bend or flatten some material (usually metal) with the round end of a ball peen hammer, or with a hammer and punch.

Valve seat inserts are usually held in position by peening the metal around them up against the insert.

A seat puller can be used to remove the old seat, but often it is necessary to break the old insert to get it out, and then use a cutting tool to take off the old peened edge.

Engines with badly worn valve seats may also show a great deal of wear on other parts. It may be less expensive to replace the engine cylinder and crankcase assembly. This is known as a short block replacement.

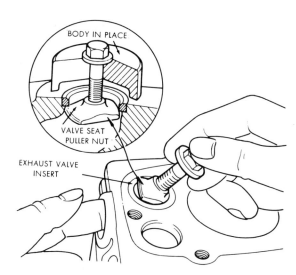

Removing a badly worn valve seat

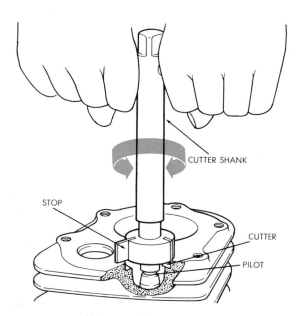

*Using a ridge cutter to
remove peened edge*

Be careful: Do not remove too much metal from the valve seat or the valve will not fit properly.

Be careful: Don't touch very cold objects or dry ice with your bare hands.

The new inserts must fit tightly to allow heat to travel quickly to the cylinder block. For this reason, a new insert is made very slightly oversize. To make it fit into its mounting hole, place it in a freezer or in dry ice for a few minutes. The cold will cause it to shrink. When it is cold enough, it will fit into the hole easily. After fitting the insert, wait until it has reached normal room temperature, then use a small ball peen hammer and a punch to peen the cylinder block as shown.

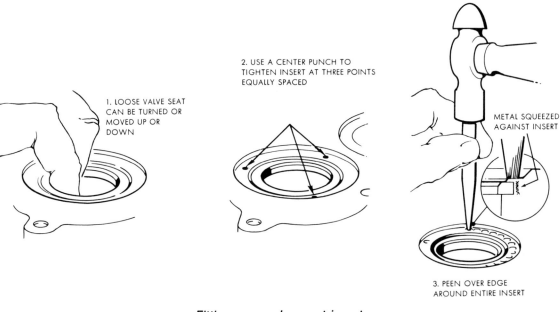

2. USE A CENTER PUNCH TO TIGHTEN INSERT AT THREE POINTS EQUALLY SPACED

1. LOOSE VALVE SEAT CAN BE TURNED OR MOVED UP OR DOWN

METAL SQUEEZED AGAINST INSERT

3. PEEN OVER EDGE AROUND ENTIRE INSERT

Fitting new valve seat insert

When installing new valve inserts or repairing old ones, the top or bottom edge of the seat should be ground off as shown, leaving a 1.5 mm ($^1/_{16}$ inch) seat width that touches the middle of the valve face. A narrow valve seat prevents carbon from building up and holding the valve open.

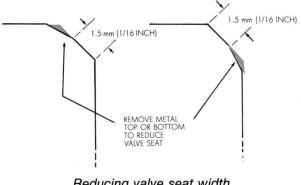

1.5 mm (1/16 INCH)

1.5 mm (1/16 INCH)

REMOVE METAL TOP OR BOTTOM TO REDUCE VALVE SEAT

Reducing valve seat width

Abrasive: a substance which can be used to slowly abrade, or wear away, some surface. The "sand" on sandpaper is an abrasive.

The drawing on the left shows a valve seat being hand lapped, with a small amount of abrasive between the seat and valve face. Move the tool back and forth between the palms of your hands until an even gray colour shows on the seat and face. Do not overdo this job.

Handlapping a valve and seat

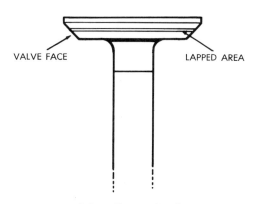

VALVE FACE   LAPPED AREA

A handlapped valve

VALVE TIMING

It is important that each valve opens and closes at exactly the right time in each cycle of operation. The exhaust valve should open when the power stroke has been completed and stay open until the piston has reached the top of the exhaust stroke. As the piston starts down on the intake stroke, the intake valve should open and remain open until the piston travels all the way to the bottom of the intake stroke. Both valves must be tightly closed during the compression and power strokes.

It is common design practice for manufacturers to allow some valve overlap between strokes when designing engines. This means that the intake valve may open two or three degrees before the actual start of the intake stroke and close as much as 35° after the stroke ends, allowing more time for the fuel to enter the cylinder. The next drawing shows the number of degrees of crankshaft revolution during which the intake valve would stay open in a typical engine.

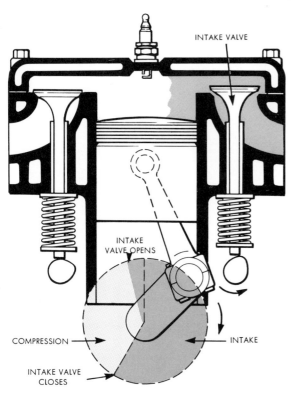

*Amount of crankshaft revolution with
intake valve open*

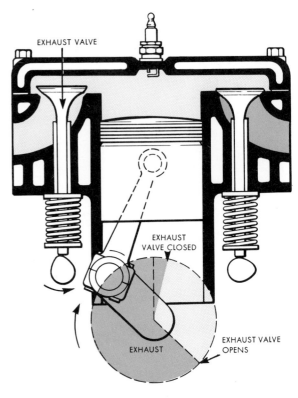

*Amount of crankshaft revolution with
exhaust valve open*

Sprocket: a wheel with teeth on its edge. The teeth catch in holes between chain links to make another wheel turn.

To allow more time for exhaust gases to escape, the exhaust valve may open 40° to 45° ahead of the exhaust stroke and close 5° late. This means both valves are open at the same time between the intake and exhaust strokes.

To do this, the crankshaft, camshaft, and valves are timed to work together. During the complete four stroke cycle of operation, each valve must open only once. The camshaft therefore must turn at half the speed of the crankshaft. The drawings show two methods used to drive the camshaft and make it revolve at exactly half the speed of the crankshaft.

The gear or chain sprocket on the camshaft is exactly twice the size of the gear or sprocket on the crankshaft and has twice the number of teeth. Whenever these parts are removed they must be replaced so the timing marks are in their original position.

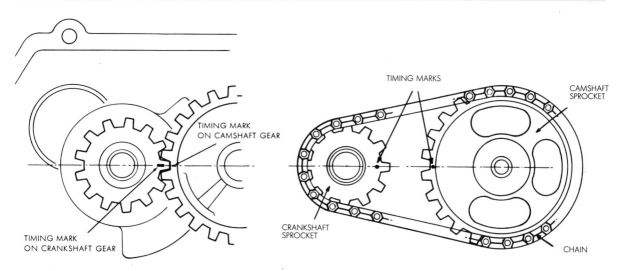

Gear method of driving camshaft   Chain and sprocket method of driving camshaft

Cam lobes on the camshaft push the valves open gradually. A strong spring pulls each valve closed after the cam moves away from the lifter.

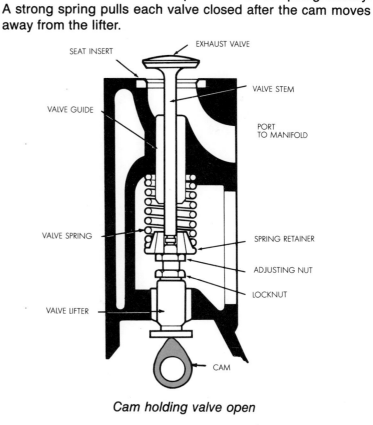

Cam holding valve open

The drawings below show three methods of holding valve springs in place on the valve stem.

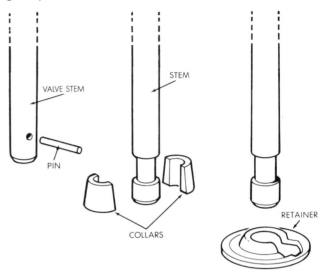

Valve spring retainers

Pistons and Piston Rings

Find the Answers to These Questions

1. From what two materials are pistons made?

2. Why are holes drilled through the piston at the bottom of the lower ring groove?

3. Why are light mass pistons so popular in modern engines?

4. What are two things about aluminum that cause piston design problems?

5. How might a plugged cooling system affect an aluminum piston?

6. What types of piston design are used to keep the piston from seizing in the cylinder? Describe these designs.

7. Name the two types of piston rings installed on pistons used in four stroke cycle engines.

8. How are some piston rings designed to put greater force against the cylinder walls?

9. Why must there be a certain amount of side clearance for a piston ring in its groove?

10. List the flaws that show a piston should be replaced.

11. What tool is used to measure piston ring end gap?

12. Why should cylinder head bolts be tightened in a particular order?

Be careful: When two people are working on the same machine, never, ever, start the engine before telling your partner. His or her hands may be in danger.

The pistons used in small four stroke cycle engines are can-shaped, with the bottom end open. The closed end is either flat or slightly rounded and is called the piston head.

Just below the head are three or four grooves to hold the piston rings. Holes drilled through the piston in the bottom groove allow oil, scraped off the cylinder walls, to return to the crankcase. The metal surrounding the open end of the piston is called the skirt and is machined to a very close fit in the cylinder to keep the piston from tilting to one side or the other. The skirt is not always square edged, as shown in the drawing of a piston with a "slipper" skirt.

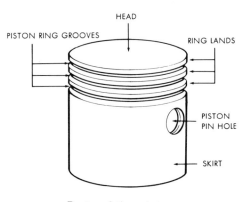

Parts of the piston

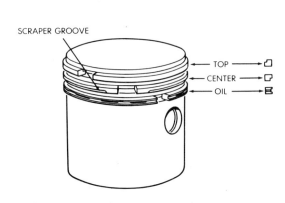

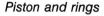

Piston and rings

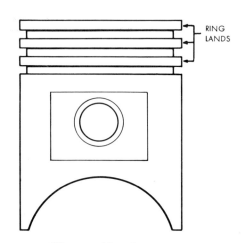

Slipper skirt piston

Alloy: a metal which has been made by mixing two or more pure metals. Brass is an alloy of copper and zinc.

Pistons are made of cast iron or aluminum alloys. The majority of the modern high speed engines use the aluminum piston because of its light mass. Since a piston must slow to a stop and reverse its direction at the end of each stroke, the light mass of aluminum becomes very important as the speed increases. Another good feature of aluminum is its ability to transfer the heat of combustion to the cylinder block more quickly than cast iron does. However, aluminum has two characteristics that cause problems. It has a low melting point, near 670°C, and a high rate of heat expansion. Poorly maintained cooling systems, or ignition systems causing heavy spark knock can cause piston failure. This failure can be a holed piston head, warped or collapsed skirt, or collapsed ring lands.

Because of the large amount of heat expansion of aluminum, pistons in the less expensive engines are fitted loosely in the cylinder, and the piston rings are used to provide the compression seal. Since this allows the piston to rattle in the cylinder until full operating temperature is reached, several other solutions have been found to the expansion problem. One of the solutions is slots cut in the skirts of pistons. These pistons can

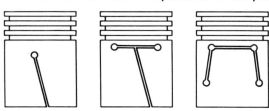

Three common slot patterns

then be machined to close fits in their cylinders. Then when the piston expands with the heat most of the expansion can be taken up by the slot, which tends to close.

Another solution is to cast steel rings into the piston, or cut away the area around the piston pin to control expansion. This is called a relieved piston.

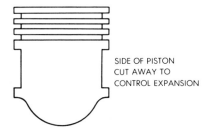

SIDE OF PISTON
CUT AWAY TO
CONTROL EXPANSION

Relieved piston

Cam grinding the piston has proved to be one of the better solutions to the problem. The piston is machined to an oval shape, with the narrow area across the pin bosses. The piston expands to a round shape at full operating temperature.

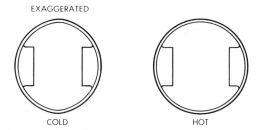

EXAGGERATED

COLD   HOT

Bottom views of cam ground piston

All of these ideas are aimed at providing a tight fitting piston, but the tightest fitting piston would still not provide a good compression seal. Whether the piston is made of aluminum or cast iron, three or four piston rings must be used to complete the seal.

PISTON RINGS

Piston rings are circles of specially treated steel, open on one side. When installed on the piston, they are free to move in the ring grooves and are made to keep a steady pressure outward against the cylinder wall. The top two rings are solid steel compression seal rings. The lower ring or rings are shaped to control the amount of oil on the cylinder wall. These rings scrape oil from the cylinder walls and return it to the crankcase. A three ring set of compression and oil control rings is shown below.

When replacing compression rings, you may find that their inside or outside edge has been cut away. This causes the ring to twist slightly in its groove, forcing one edge more tightly against the cylinder wall. Follow the piston ring manufacturer's instructions carefully to avoid installing this style of ring upside down.

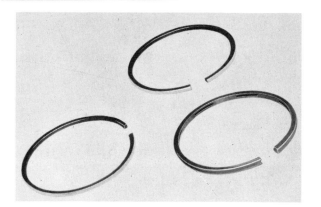

Piston ring set

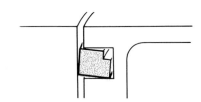

Section view of compression ring in its groove, showing twist effect

The piston rings on many pistons are held in position by small pins. This stops the rings from turning so their end gaps are in line. Compression leakage through the gaps is reduced. The drawing shows three locations of the pins in the ring grooves.

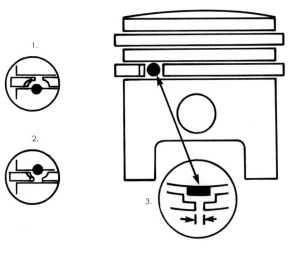

Piston ring locating pins

INSTALLING PISTON RINGS

1. Drain the oil from the crankcase and remove the crankcase cover and cylinder head.

2. Remove the connecting rod cap and push the connecting rod and piston out of the cylinder. Note the cap alignment marks and their position. They must be replaced in the original position later.

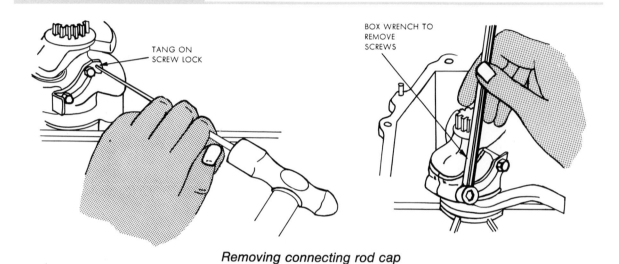

Removing connecting rod cap

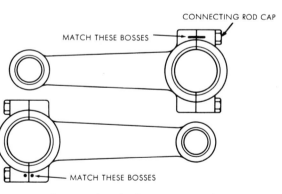

Cap and rod alignment marks

Be careful: The sides of the ring grooves must not be damaged. Do not scratch or dent the grooves.

3. Clean the connecting rod and piston assembly. Use a ring groove cleaner or the end of a broken piston ring to remove dirt and carbon from the ring grooves.

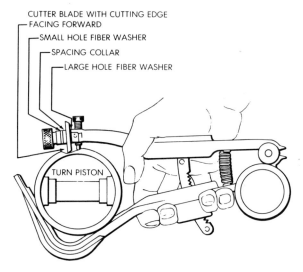

Carbon removal tool in use

4. Replace a piston if it is collapsed or if it shows ring lands that are cracked or chipped, ring grooves that are worn beyond allowable clearances, or a cracked skirt or head. The drawing below shows ring groove clearance being checked with a feeler gauge.

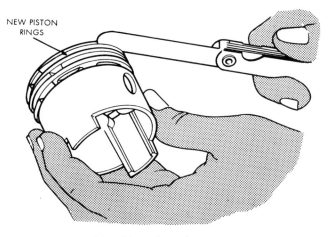

Checking ring clearance

Use a micrometer at two or more points around the piston to check for out-of-round condition. You should get the same reading. Remember that some pistons have been cam ground and are supposed to be out of round. Check the engine repair manual.

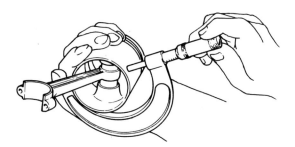

Checking piston for roundness

5. Check the cylinder for scuffing or score marks. These conditions can be corrected with a cylinder hone if the damage is light.

Hone: an abrasive tool used to enlarge holes and make them very accurate. If a fine abrasive is used, the finish will be very smooth.

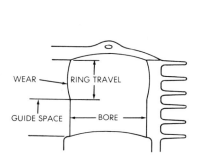

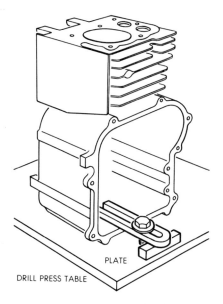

Engine set up for honing

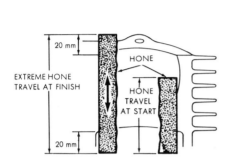

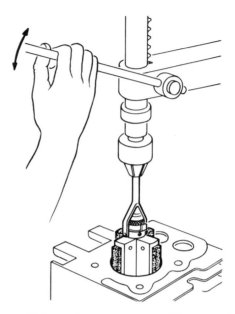

Using a hone to re-condition a cylinder

Some manufacturers and mechanics do not like using a hone in aluminum cylinders because bits of abrasive may become stuck in the soft metal. The piston and new rings would then be quickly damaged.

6. If the cylinder does not need honing, remove any ridge that may be found at the top of the cylinder with a ridge remover. This ridge occurs because no ring wear is taking place at the very top of the cylinder. Often it is necessary to remove the ridge in order to slide the piston out of the cylinder.

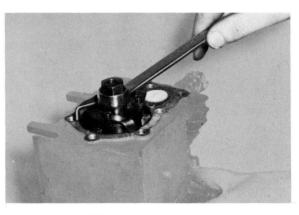

Ridge remover in use

Be careful: Piston rings break easily.

7. Check the amount of piston ring end gap of each new ring by pushing it into the lower cylinder with the head of the piston. Use a feeler gauge as shown. If the gap is smaller than the manufacturer says it should be, carefully file one end of the ring. Remove any burr that the file may cause, then push the ring back in the cylinder and check the end gap again.

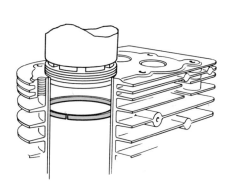

New ring pushed into the cylinder with the piston

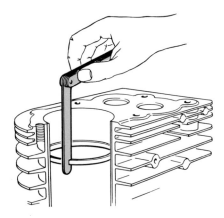

Checking the end gauge clearance of a new piston ring

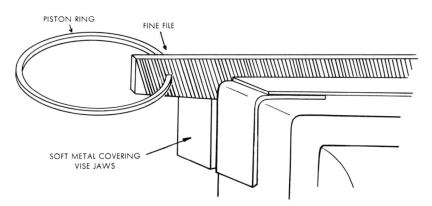

PISTON RING

FINE FILE

SOFT METAL COVERING VISE JAWS

Making the ring gap the correct size

8. Install the new rings on the piston with a ring tool to avoid breaking or bending them. Arrange the end gaps so they are not one above the other.

Be careful: If the end gaps of the piston rings are above each other they will form a hole that oil, air, and fuel can go through.

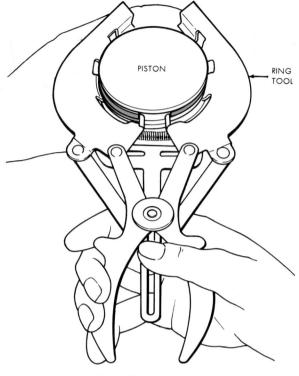

Installing new rings

9. Use a piston ring compressor to install the piston in the cylinder. Some pistons are marked to show the correct position in the cylinder. Check the engine manual.

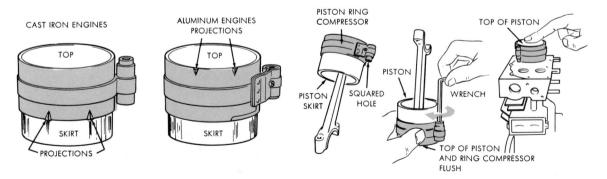

Installing piston with piston ring compressor

Be careful: Turn the crankshaft to make sure the connecting rod is clear of all other engine parts; then lock the cap bolts in place. The rod may be made to clear when facing one way only.

10. Install the connecting rod cap so the alignment marks match and are in the same position as before. Some caps and rods have no marks but are made to fit in one position only. Tighten the cap bolts to the specified torque.

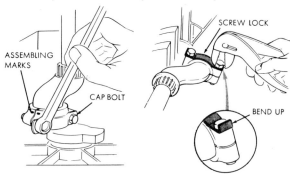

11. Bend the lugs of any lug-type lock washer or strap to prevent the bolts from working loose.

12. Replace the crankcase cover and cylinder head, using new gaskets, and fill the crankcase with oil to the correct level.

Use a torque wrench to tighten all cylinder head and crankcase bolts. Refer to a tightness chart for the particular engine you are repairing. Do not over-tighten.

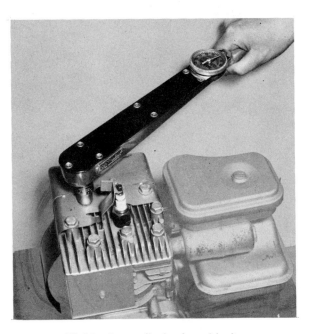

Tightening cylinder head bolts

Cylinder head bolts should be tightened in a definite pattern to prevent warping of the head. When no instruction is available, any pattern that avoids tightening two adjacent bolts one after the other can be used. The drawings show two head bolt patterns used on small engines.

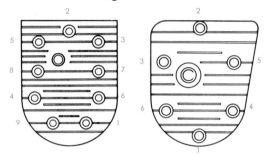

Head bolt patterns

Things to Do

1. Remove the cylinder head from a small four stroke engine. Turn the crankshaft slowly by hand and watch the action of the valves during each of the four strokes. Notice the intake and exhaust valve overlap.

2. Remove one or both valves as described in the text. Examine the condition of the face, margin, and stem of the valve. Do the valves wobble in their guides?

3. Replace the valves, valve springs, and retainers and measure the clearance between the valve stem and the lifter. Compare this measurement to the engine specifications.

4. Remove the crankcase cover and locate the valve timing marks on the timing gears.

5. Remove the piston and connecting rod assembly, as described in the text. Measure piston ring side clearance. Remove one ring and measure its end gap.

6. Clean all parts and re-assemble the engine. Use a torque wrench to tighten all bolts.

A four stroke cycle engine with gear box to slow down the shaft speed

CHAPTER 4

TWO STROKE CYCLE ENGINES

Watch for These Words

lubrication
reed
rotary
sump

diesel
vacuum
ports
carbon

How to Use These Words

1. Two stroke cycle engines get their *lubrication* by having oil mixed with their fuel.

2. *Reed* valves and *rotary* valves are used in small two stroke cycle engines instead of poppet valves.

3. Small two stroke cycle engines do not need a *sump* to hold oil.

4. Heat from very high compression starts the fuel burning in *diesel* engine cylinders.

5. Air pressure works to fill any *vacuum* in an engine.

6. The exhaust *ports* of two stroke cycle engines may get plugged with *carbon*.

Be careful: Gasoline fumes are explosive. Always mix gasoline and oil outside.

A light weight mower powered by a two stroke cycle engine

Diesel: a type of engine where fuel is injected into very hot compressed air to be ignited, instead of being mixed with air before compression and ignition.

Port: a hole in a cylinder wall, designed to let fuel and air in, or exhaust gases out.

Look for Answers to These Questions

1. How often does the crankshaft revolve during the two stroke cycle?
2. Why is the exhaust port higher in the cylinder than the intake port?
3. What causes the reed valve to open, allowing fuel to enter the crankcase?
4. When, during the cycle of operation, does the reed valve close?
5. Which of the two strokes is the power stroke?
6. What other part of the operating cycle takes place on this stroke?
7. How are two stroke cycle engines lubricated?
8. Why does the piston head sometimes have a special shape?
9. Why is there no need for an oil control piston ring?
10. Why are two stroke cycle engines usually lighter in mass then four stroke cycle engines of the same power rating?

Two Stroke Cycle Engines

The two stroke cycle engine is simpler in design than the four stroke cycle engine. It has many uses, ranging from the smallest model aircraft engine to large two stroke diesel engines in buses, trucks, and trains. Although it looks very much like a four stroke engine, a two stroke cycle engine works in a different way.

The simplest two stroke cycle engine has only three moving and wear-producing parts. These parts are the piston, the connecting rod, and the crankshaft. All the intake and exhaust work is done by making the piston cover or uncover holes or ports in the cylinder wall. The piston actually takes the place of valves, doing the same job as the poppet valves in a four stroke engine.

In Chapter Three we learned that all internal combustion engines do four separate actions in order to operate. These actions are intake, compression, power and exhaust. In four stroke cycle engines these actions are performed on separate strokes of the piston. The two stroke design performs the four basic operating actions with only two strokes of the piston. Every *down* stroke is a power and exhaust stroke and every *up* stroke is an intake and compression stroke.

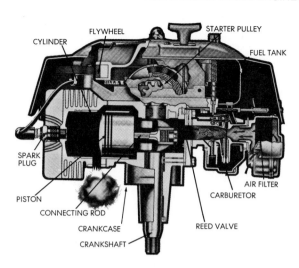

CYLINDER · FLYWHEEL · STARTER PULLEY · FUEL TANK · AIR FILTER · CARBURETOR · REED VALVE · CRANKSHAFT · CRANKCASE · CONNECTING ROD · PISTON · SPARK PLUG

Cutaway drawing of a two stroke cycle engine

THE INTAKE – COMPRESSION STROKE

As the piston begins to move up in the cylinder, it covers the intake and exhaust ports and starts to compress the fuel/air charge in the upper part of the cylinder. At the same time, a vacuum is caused in the crankcase below the piston. The vacuum creates suction on a flat piece of spring steel, called a reed valve. The suction opens the valve, and fuel and air rush in from the carburetor.

Vacuum: an area of very low air pressure. Air always tries to fill a vacuum, if it can.

Reed: a thin, flat, strip of spring metal.

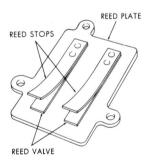

REED PLATE · REED STOPS · REED VALVE

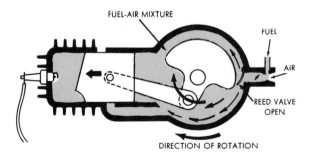

FUEL-AIR MIXTURE · FUEL · AIR · REED VALVE OPEN · DIRECTION OF ROTATION

The intake-compression stroke

As the piston nears the top of the stroke, the spark plug fires and the fuel begins to burn.

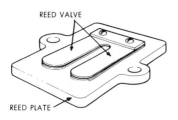

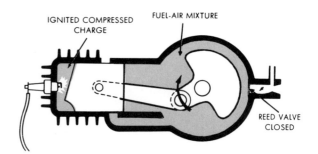

The intake-compression stroke ending

THE POWER – EXHAUST STROKE

The burning fuel creates heat and pressure in the combustion chamber, and pushes the piston down on the power stroke. The downward motion of the piston causes pressure in the crankcase. The reed valve closes as the vacuum disappears, and the fuel/air mixture in the crankcase is compressed.

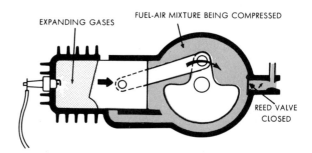

The power-exhaust stroke beginning

Near the end of the down stroke, the piston uncovers the exhaust port, allowing the burned gases to escape. Still further down it uncovers the intake port. The fuel mixture that has been compressed in the crankcase now rushes into the cylinder through the intake port and the intake-compression stroke begins.

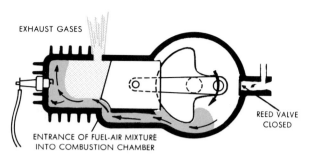

EXHAUST GASES

ENTRANCE OF FUEL-AIR MIXTURE
INTO COMBUSTION CHAMBER

REED VALVE
CLOSED

The power-exhaust stroke ending

Rotary: turning on shaft.

A few engines use a rotary valve instead of reed valves to control fuel intake into the crankcase. This valve may be a hole in a hollowed out crankshaft or a disc with a hole in it that turns with the crankshaft and opens and closes the carburetor opening.

ROTARY VALVE OPENING

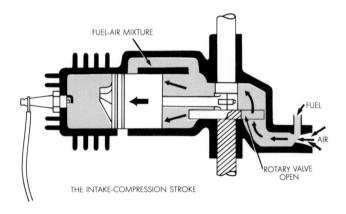

FUEL-AIR MIXTURE

FUEL

AIR

ROTARY VALVE
OPEN

THE INTAKE-COMPRESSION STROKE

ROTARY VALVE OPEN

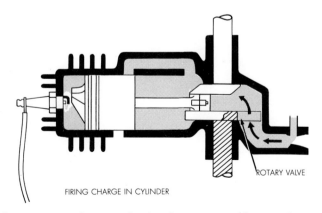

ROTARY VALVE

FIRING CHARGE IN CYLINDER

A two stroke cycle engine with a rotary valve, on the intake-compression stroke

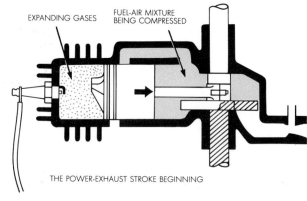

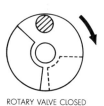

ROTARY VALVE CLOSED

EXPANDING GASES

FUEL-AIR MIXTURE BEING COMPRESSED

THE POWER-EXHAUST STROKE BEGINNING

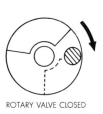

ROTARY VALVE CLOSED

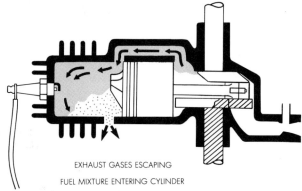

EXHAUST GASES ESCAPING

FUEL MIXTURE ENTERING CYLINDER

A two stroke cycle engine with a rotary valve, on the power-exhaust stroke of the two stroke cycle

A two cylinder, two stroke cycle engine used to power an ultralight aircraft

Two Stroke Cycle Cylinder Design

Single cylinder, air-cooled, two stroke cycle engines usually have a one-piece cylinder and cylinder head. This unit is called a cylinder pot. There is no need for a separate cylinder head, since there are no valves to remove or repair.

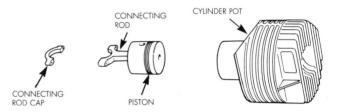

Cylinder pot and piston assembly from an air-cooled two stroke engine

Be careful: Be sure the engine is not running when filling the fuel tank.

Chainsaws are powered by two stroke cycle engines.

Water-cooled two stroke engines, as used for most outboard boat engines, have a removable cylinder head. This is because it is difficult to make a one piece cylinder pot with water passages in the head and cylinder walls.

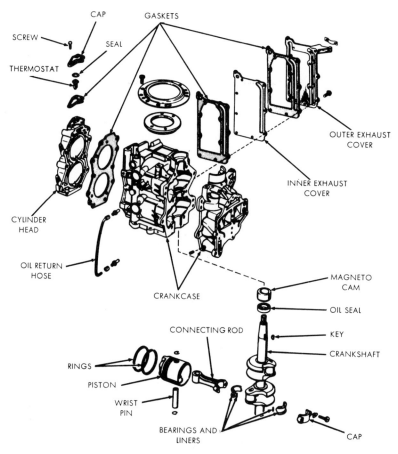

The parts of a two cylinder outboard boat engine

The intake and exhaust ports are positioned opposite each other, with the exhaust opening slightly higher in the cylinder in most models. This allows most of the exhaust gases and combustion pressure to escape before the new fuel charge enters the cylinder.

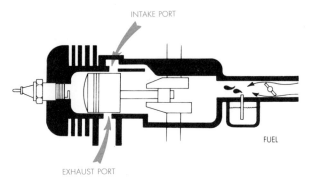

Intake and exhaust ports

Carbon: a hard, black material, formed when too much fuel is mixed with air in a cylinder.

An engine that lacks power and is hard to start may have its exhaust ports partly plugged with carbon. This can be removed with a screwdriver when the piston covers the port. Do not scratch the piston.

Be careful: Do not scratch the piston when removing carbon deposits from around the exhaust port. Be sure the piston wall covers the port.

Removing carbon from exhaust ports

CRANKCASE DESIGN

Sump: a container for oil or other liquids.

The crankcase of the two stroke cycle engine is specially designed. The interior allows just enough room for free movement of the crankshaft and connecting rod. No oil sump is

Lubrication: adding grease or oil to an engine so that moving parts slide easily and quickly without getting too hot. Oil is a very good lubricant.

needed, since all lubrication is taken care of by a small amount of oil mixed with the gasoline. This method of lubrication is described in Chapter Six.

Keeping the crankcase small means that a greater vacuum can be created by the upward motion of the piston. This causes the reed valve to open more quickly and wider for fuel intake. Higher compression of the fuel/air mixture, in the crankcase, also becomes possible.

In order to get the best possible performance from a two stroke cycle engine, all crankshaft bearing seals and gasket sealed joints must be leakproof. It is always a good idea to use all new gaskets when re-assembling a two stroke engine.

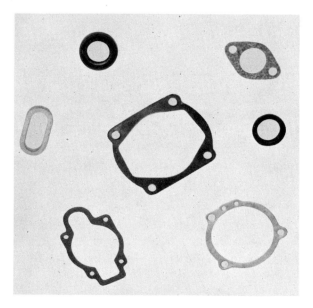

Gasket set

PISTON DESIGN

A piston in a two stroke cycle engine does the job of opening and closing the intake and exhaust ports, as well as transferring power to the connecting rod and crankshaft. Special piston head shapes are often used to help the exhaust gases escape and to direct the incoming fuel toward the top of the cylinder. This reduces the amount of fuel lost through the exhaust port before it is fired by the spark plug.

The skirt of the piston must be long enough to cover the ports when the piston is at the top of its stroke and must fit closely enough to seal the ports completely.

PISTON RINGS

Since all lubrication of the two stroke engine is taken care of by the oil mixed with the fuel, there is no need for an oil control ring. Thus, there are usually only two compression rings installed on the piston to seal the cylinder.

An engine with so few moving parts will last a long time if care is always taken to mix the fuel accurately. Using more oil than the manufacturer says to will cause hard starting and a drop in power. Using too little oil will cause the bearings to wear quickly. It will also cause scraping and scoring of the cylinder walls. The piston may even seize in the cylinder. The piston rings cannot seal a piston in a badly damaged cylinder. On some engines the only repair possible is to replace the worn parts.

INTAKE SIDE   EXHAUST SIDE

 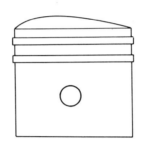 

Pistons used in two stroke cycle engines

Things To Do

1. Carefully take a two stroke cycle engine apart or use a cut-away model to locate the parts listed:

   (a) crankcase
   (b) cylinder
   (c) intake port
   (d) exhaust port
   (e) reed valve
   (f) crankshaft
   (g) connecting rod and cap
   (h) piston and piston pin
   (i) piston rings
   (j) carburetor

2. Examine a reed valve and its mounting plate. The reed valve should fit tightly against the plate. If it does not fit tightly, try turning it over on the mounting plate.

3. Mix a container of fuel with the amount of oil specified by the maker of the engine. Most engines use 1 litre of oil to 20 litres of gasoline (6 ounces of oil to a gallon of gasoline).

4. Look for carbon-plugged exhaust ports in one or more two stroke engines. Clean the ports carefully.

CHAPTER 5

ENGINE COOLING SYSTEMS

Watch for These Words

temperature	*anti-freeze*
thermostat	*shroud*
radiator	

How to Use These Words

1. The *temperature* of the coolant in liquid-cooled engines is controlled by the *thermostat*.

2. Air moving through a *radiator* cools the liquid for many engines.

3. When water is used to cool an engine, some *anti-freeze* must be added to keep it from freezing in the winter.

4. A sheet metal *shroud* directs cooling air past the cylinder of an air-cooled engine.

Look for Answers to These Questions

1. Why do internal combustion engines need cooling systems?
2. What two types of cooling systems are used in these engines?
3. a) Why are fins needed on an air-cooled engine?
   b) How is the air forced over these fins?
4. Why do water-cooled engines usually have a pump?
5. Give an example of an air-cooled engine which would need cleaning often.
6. Give an example of a water-cooled engine that uses no radiator.

WHY ENGINES MUST HAVE COOLING SYSTEMS

Temperature: a measurement of the hotness or coldness of something.

An internal combustion engine is a heat engine. It gets its power from the heat produced by the burning mixture of gasoline and air in its cylinder. The temperature inside the cylinder can be as high as 2200°C (4500°F) during the power stroke.

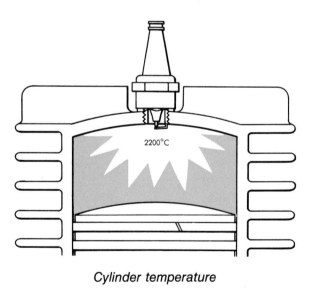

2200°C

Cylinder temperature

A small motorcycle with a liquid cooled engine. Notice the cooling radiator.

Some of this heat gets away through the exhaust opening on the exhaust stroke, but most of it is soaked up by the cylinder walls, cylinder head, and piston. If they were not cooled in some way, these metal parts would soon soften and melt, or at least would expand to the point where the piston would be too big for the cylinder and would become stuck to the cylinder wall. If a piston gets stuck in a cylinder a lot of damage occurs, which is difficult and often impossible to repair.

WATER COOLING

A water-cooled engine is made so that its cylinders are surrounded by hollow passages. This "water jacket," as it is called, is kept filled with cool water.

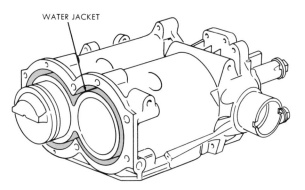

The water jacket around the twin cylinders of an outboard engine

Modern engines have a pump that forces the water to move through the water jacket from a radiator. A fan is mounted behind the radiator to draw air through it and cool the water. This helps to keep the engine cool.

When water freezes, it expands. In other words, it takes up more space as ice than it did as water. In winter, water often freezes. If it freezes and expands in an engine's water jacket it can damage the engine. For this reason a liquid anti-freeze must be added. This anti-freeze should be a permanent type that contains a rust preventer and lubricant. It should be used in summer as well as winter since it also raises the boiling point of the water coolant.

Radiator: a device designed to radiate or give up heat into the air. House heating systems often have radiators, too.

Anti-freeze: a liquid which has lower freezing and higher boiling points than water. It prevents engines from freezing.

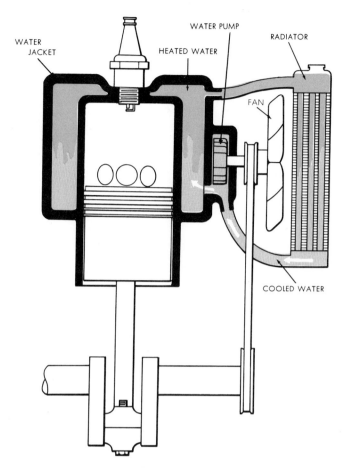

WATER PUMP
WATER JACKET
HEATED WATER
RADIATOR
FAN
COOLED WATER

A fan and radiator being used to cool the water for an engine water jacket

Outboard engines for small boats are water-cooled but have no radiators. Their supply of cooling water is pumped from the water in which the boat is floating. All test running of outboard engines must be done with the propeller and water inlet in a tank of water.

The diagram at the top of page 88 shows the water passages through the lower unit, cylinder, and head of an outboard boat engine.

A water cooled engine for small boats

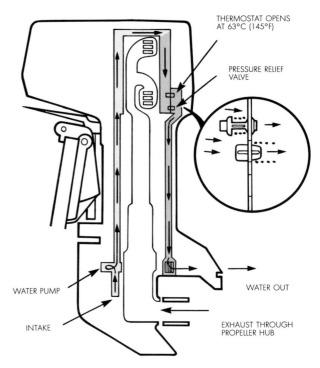

THERMOSTAT OPENS
AT 63°C (145°F)

PRESSURE RELIEF
VALVE

WATER PUMP

INTAKE

WATER OUT

EXHAUST THROUGH
PROPELLER HUB

Water passage through a large outboard motor

A water pump lifts cold water into the engine water jacket. There, the cold water picks up heat from the cylinder walls. The water is then forced back into the lake or river.

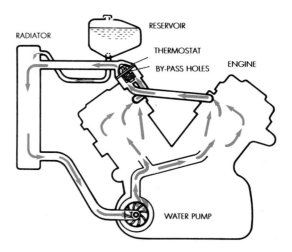

RADIATOR

RESERVOIR

THERMOSTAT

BY-PASS HOLES

ENGINE

WATER PUMP

The location of the water pump and thermostat in a liquid cooled motorcycle engine. The thermostat begins to open at 75°C (167°F) and is fully open at 90°C (194°F).

COOLING WATER INLET

DIRECTION OF
ROTATION

COOLING WATER
TO CYLINDER BLOCK

PUMP OUTLET

RUBBER PUMP IMPELLER

One type of water pump operating at low speed

If an engine is cooled too much, fuel will not burn properly in the cylinder. The cylinder and spark plug will quickly become coated with carbon, and fuel will be wasted. The spark will not jump between carbon-covered spark plug electrodes. Small bits of carbon in a cylinder may heat red hot and ignite the fuel before the spark plug fires. Bits of carbon can scratch cylinder walls and piston rings.

To prevent the water from cooling the engine too much, a thermostat is installed in the water jacket to control the flow of water. The thermostat holds the water back until it reaches a warmer temperature. It then opens to allow the heated water to escape and cool water to flow in. Some of the water is bypassed through a control valve and returned to the water pump.

A thermostat must be installed facing the right way. Most are labelled to show the side facing the engine.

A screen filter on the water intake keeps weeds, sticks, small fish, and dirt out of the cooling system. This screen should be checked and cleaned before each use of the engine. If the screen gets plugged, the engine will soon overheat and possibly seize up.

Thermostat: a device used to control the temperature of an engine. If the engine is too cold it holds back heat until the engine is hot enough. It then lets heat escape.

AIR COOLING

Most small single cylinder engines are cooled by a stream of air blown by a fan over and around the cylinder and cylinder head. The fan is often part of the flywheel, and a sheet metal covering called a shroud is used to direct the air where it is needed.

The cylinder head and outside of the cylinder block are covered with fins so that more metal surface comes in contact with the air. The heat from the cylinder is then carried away more quickly.

Shroud: a covering which acts to direct cooling air.

Be careful: If dirt builds up between the cooling fins, the engine will overheat.

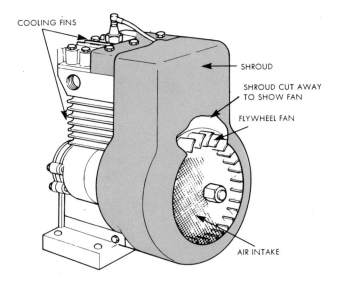

Shroud and intake screen cut away to show fan blades

Maintenance of Cooling Systems

WATER COOLING SYSTEMS

1. Check the water level in the radiator often, and keep it filled to 25 mm (1 inch) from the top or as shown in the manufacturer's manual.
2. Drain the water at the end of each season and refill with clean water.
3. Add a rust inhibitor during the summer months. Most good anti-freeze solutions include rust inhibitors for winter use.
4. Inspect the hoses for cracks or softness and replace them in either case.

AIR COOLING SYSTEMS

1. Keep the spaces between the cooling fins clean. If dirt and oil fill up these spaces, the air cannot touch the metal surface. Overheating will be the result.
2. The air intake screen must be kept clean.
3. Do not operate an air-cooled engine for any length of time without its shroud in place.

Things To Do

1. Remove the shroud from a lawnmower engine and clean the cooling fins with a stiff brush, a cloth, and a putty knife. Replace the shroud.
2. Remove the water pump from an outboard engine; clean the intake screen, the rotor, and the housing. Replace all parts carefully.
3. Look at some cooling system thermostats. Test them using a thermometer in a pail of water. Heat the water and watch to see at which temperature the thermostats open.

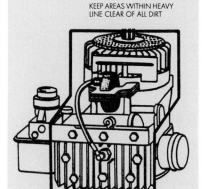

KEEP AREAS WITHIN HEAVY LINE CLEAR OF ALL DIRT

Engine shroud removed to show areas to be kept clean

CHAPTER 6

ENGINE LUBRICATION

Words to Learn

refineries   viscosity
friction   additives
bearing   power

How to Use These Words

1. Oil *refineries* are large factories that make many products from crude oil.
2. Lubricating oil is used in engines to reduce *friction* between *bearing* parts.
3. High *viscosity* oil is thicker than low viscosity oil.
4. Engine cleaning *additives* are added to heavy duty oil.
5. The output of an engine is described as the *power* it produces.

Look for Answers to These Questions

1. List three reasons why engines must be lubricated.
2. What is the meaning of the word *viscosity*?
3. Why is a higher viscosity oil sometimes used in summer than in winter?
4. What stops oil from leaking out around the crankshaft and between the crankcase joints?

5. What two types of bearings are used in small engines?

6. What two lubrication systems are used in small four stroke cycle engines?

7. What method is used to lubricate small two stroke cycle engines?

WHY ENGINES NEED OIL

Bearing: the surface of any part of a machine on which another part turns or moves.

Oil provides a thin coating over all moving parts of the engine. This thin coating is called a film. Sometimes this oil film is only 0.025 mm (1/1000 inch) thick, but it still holds bearing surfaces apart and stops them from rubbing together and wearing.

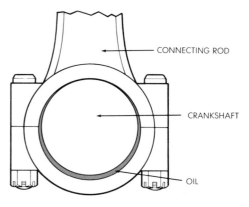

Oil film in bearing

Friction: the resistance you can feel when you rub two things together.

Oil helps to control the temperature of bearings and other engine parts. It does this by reducing *friction* between parts and by carrying heat away from the piston and cylinder walls.

As the oil splashes about or moves through bearings and along cylinder walls, it washes everything clean. Bits of carbon and fine metal chips can be drained from the engine with every oil change.

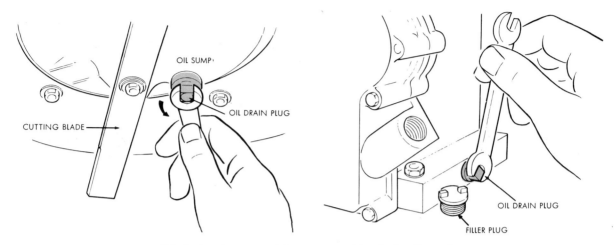

Oil drain plugs must be removed to drain dirty oil.
Refill the crankcase with the correct oil.

Oil also seals the tiny space between the piston rings and the cylinder wall. The fuel can then be compressed more tightly into the cylinder, the pressure of the expanding burning gases cannot escape past the piston rings, and the engine is more powerful.

ENGINE BEARINGS

Bearings are special surfaces made to hold revolving shafts, such as crankshafts, or to act as guides for sliding parts, such as pistons and piston rings, or to control end to end movement of shafts.

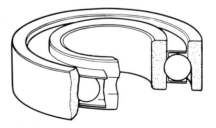

Ball type bearing cut away to show inside

Some bearings are friction bearings, which depend entirely on lubricating oil to reduce wear, while others are non-friction bearings. Non-friction bearings use hard steel rollers or balls to prevent wear. Non-friction bearings must also be lubricated with oil. The drawing shows two common locations for friction and non-friction bearings.

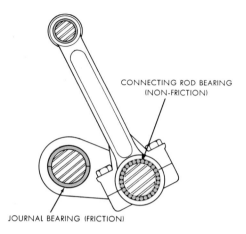

Common locations of friction and non-friction bearings

When repairing an engine, always check the oil passages to the bearings to be sure they are not full of dirty oil sludge.

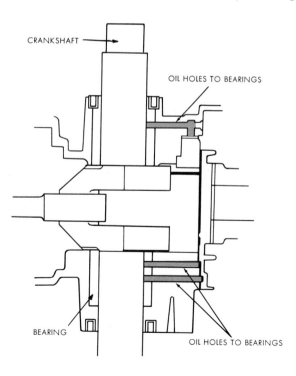

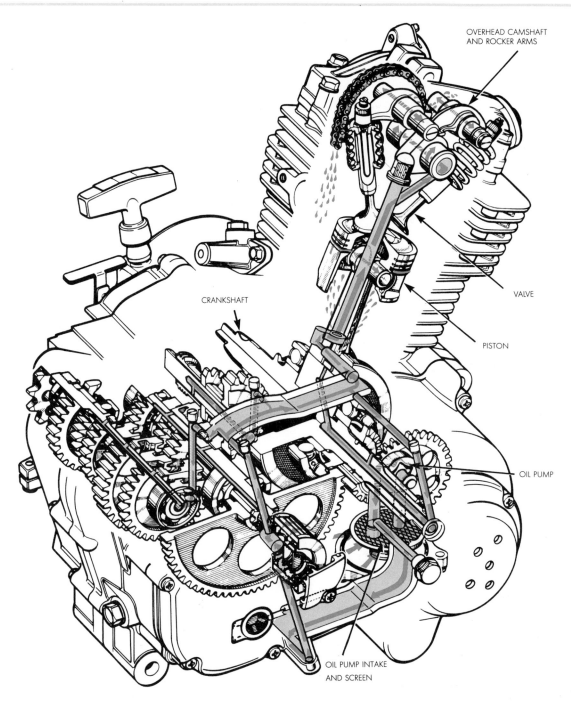

OVERHEAD CAMSHAFT
AND ROCKER ARMS

VALVE

PISTON

OIL PUMP

CRANKSHAFT

OIL PUMP INTAKE
AND SCREEN

*The arrows show the oil passages through a small motorcycle
engine and transmission.*

Oil seals around crankshafts should be replaced when you can see small amounts of oil on the shaft.

When an engine has been taken apart for repair, all of the gaskets between engine parts should be replaced. New gaskets prevent leaks.

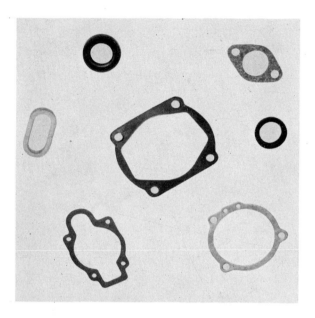

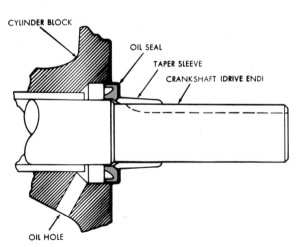

Installing a new bearing oil seal

What Is Oil?

Refineries: factories where crude oil is broken down into several products.

The oil that we use to lubricate engines is only a part of the crude oil that is pumped from the earth and transported by tank trucks, rail cars, and pipelines to *refineries.* Gasoline, fuel oil, kerosene, and wax are only a few of the hundreds of products made from crude oil.

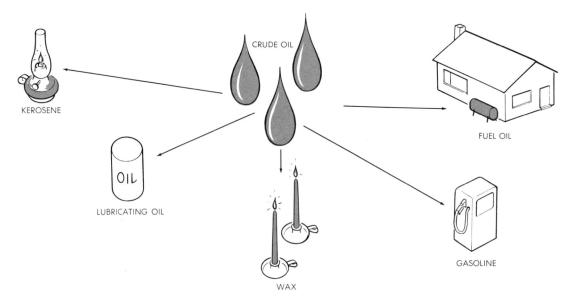

CRUDE OIL

KEROSENE

LUBRICATING OIL

WAX

FUEL OIL

GASOLINE

Products made from crude oil

OIL VISCOSITY

Viscosity: a word that means how thick or thin a liquid is.

On every can of lubricating oil are the letters S.A.E., followed by a number. These initials stand for the Society of Automotive Engineers, which controls the *viscosity* ratings of oil. "Viscosity" means thickness, or the ability of a liquid to be poured. The numbers indicate the viscosity rating. The larger the number the thicker the oil is and the harder it is to pour. S.A.E. 10 oil will pour more easily than S.A.E. 20.

Oil usually gets thin when it is hot and thick when it is cold, so some people use a low viscosity oil in the winter and a high viscosity oil in summer. Some modern oils are designed to resist temperature changes and stay the same in any weather. Engine manufacturers often suggest high viscosity oil such as SAE 30 or SAE 10W-30 for summer use and lower viscosity oil such as SAE 20 or SAE 5W-20 for winter use.

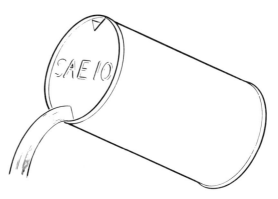

Viscosity = ''pourability''

LIGHT AND HEAVY DUTY OIL

The American Petroleum Institute groups engine oil into two classes, based on the use the oil will get. The two classes are known as service classes. The service classes are (1) Service Station oils for use in gasoline engines, and (2) Commercial oils for use in diesel engines. These two classes are each broken down into different types of oil. You can tell the types apart by the letters on the top of the can.

In the Service Station class of oils, the letters SA on the top of the can show that it contains oil for use in utility engines doing light work where dust, dirt and corrosion are not a problem.

The letters SB tell us the oil is made for minimum duty gasoline engine service where some high speed work may be done. There are no engine cleaning detergents in either SA or SB oils.

SC oil is for medium duty engines. These oils are made to cut down on dirt and carbon deposits in the engine, as well as rust and corrosion of bearing surfaces.

SD and SE oils have even more ability to resist engine wear, especially in very cold, hot, or dusty conditions.

Mechanics of small engines use SE heavy duty oil in all four stroke cycle engines, and in many two stroke cycle engines. Special problems are found when automotive oils must be mixed with gasoline for two stroke cycle engines. Most oil companies and at least one engine manufacturer make and sell a heavy duty oil. This oil is made to be used only in two stroke cycle engines. Follow the directions carefully when you mix it with gasoline.

Commercial oils for diesel use are made in four classes, from light duty CA, to CD for the largest and heaviest duty engines.

Oil should be changed after each twenty-five hours of engine use, or more often when there has been a great deal of dust and dirt around the engine. When an engine is working, small bits of metal from the cylinder walls, pistons and bearings gradually work into the oil. Dust from the air also gets into the oil. If the oil is not changed regularly, these tiny pieces of dust and metal will act like sandpaper on all moving parts. The life of the engine will be much shorter. Oil gradually thickens as it becomes dirty and loses much of its cooling ability.

Engine Lubrication Systems

SPLASH LUBRICATION

In many small four stroke engines, the bearings and cylinder walls are oiled by means of a dipper rod attached to the bottom of the connecting rod.

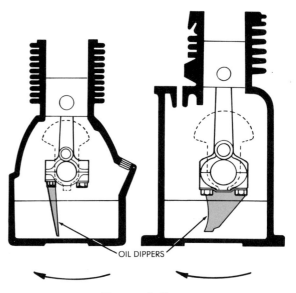

OIL DIPPERS

Types of dippers

Be careful: Protect your eyes. Wear safety glasses.

The dipper splashes oil up from the crankcase with every turn of the crankshaft. Other, more expensive, engines have a paddle wheel, driven by the timing gears, that splashes oil where it is needed. The paddle wheel is called a slinger.

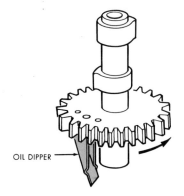

Oil dipper on cam gear

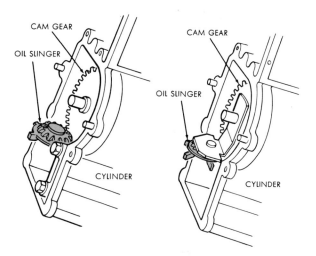

Oil slingers — splash lubrication

PRESSURE LUBRICATION

Small four stroke engines of 2.2 kW (3 horsepower) and more are often lubricated by a small pump. This pump is driven by the timing gears. It pushes oil from the crankcase through small holes and passages to the bearings and the oil control ring on the piston.

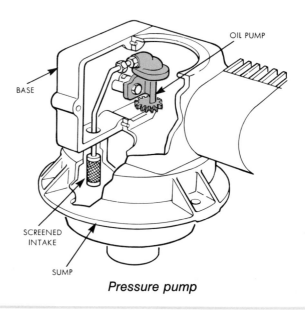

Pressure pump

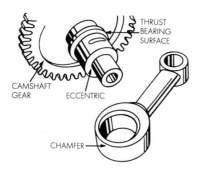

A plunger type oil pump operated by an eccentric on the camshaft

A cutaway view of a plunger oil pump

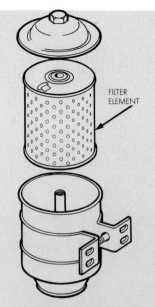

FILTER ELEMENT

A can type oil filter with a replaceable element

Additives: chemicals which are added to oil to help make it perform better in the engine.

OIL FILTERS

Engines that are likely to be operated in dirty, dusty conditions may be fitted with an oil filter. As the engine oil passes through the filter, it holds the dirt and dust that would otherwise cause wear on bearing surfaces. The filter element should be replaced when the engine oil is changed.

OIL MIXED WITH GASOLINE

All small two stroke engines that draw fuel through the crankcase to the cylinder are lubricated by adding oil to the gasoline. The oil and fuel mixture touches every part in the crankcase before being burned in the cylinder. Since oil burns slowly, some of it stays in the combustion chamber to lubricate the upper cylinder.

The oil used in these engines is called "outboard motor oil", and has special *additives.* These reduce carbon and oil fouling of the spark plug and cylinder and make the oil mix more easily with the gasoline. This oil is about S.A.E. 30 viscosity. Engine manufacturers usually say how much of it should be added to the gasoline for their particular engines. Fifty mL of oil to a litre of gasoline is common. Cans of this oil are marked BIA TC-W. BIA means Boating Industry Association, and TC-W means Two Cycle Water-cooled.

Things To Do

1. Find two or more products made from crude oil that are not mentioned in the text.

2. Name three lubricating methods used in small engines.

3. Find out why gaskets should not be re-used.

4. Change the oil in a four stroke cycle engine. Check the engine manual for the amount and the viscosity of the oil you should use.

5. Read the engine manuals for two or more brands of two stroke cycle engines. Compare the amounts of outboard engine oil and gasoline that should be mixed together for each engine. Are they the same?

CHAPTER 7

CARBURETION

Watch for These Words

governor	*filter*
throttle	*jet*
gravity	*venturi*
vent	*diaphragm*
solvent	*suction*
mesh	

How to Use These Words

1. The *governor* controls the *throttle* in a carburetor.

2. When the fuel tank is above the carburetor, the force of *gravity* will make the fuel flow down into the float bowl.

3. Most fuel tank caps have a *vent* hole to allow air to enter as the fuel is used up.

4. Use a *solvent* to clean the fine wire *mesh* in an oil bath air *filter.*

5. The main fuel *jet* is always located in the *venturi* of a carburetor.

6. The *diaphragm* in a fuel pump causes *suction* in the fuel line to draw fuel from the tank.

Look for Answers to These Questions

1. What is the purpose of a carburetor?

2. What is a venturi?

3. What prevents gasoline from overflowing into the throat of a gravity feed carburetor?

4. What style of carburetor would be the least expensive to manufacture and repair?

5. Why does the idle circuit need its own separate fuel and air supply?

6. What part of the carburetor controls the speed of the engine?

7. How does the choke change the fuel/air mixture for easier starting of a cold engine?

8. Why is the air cleaner such an important part of the engine?

9. Name three styles of carburetor air cleaners.

GASOLINE

Liquid gasoline is a substance that burns in air with a cool yellow flame and much black smoke. Compared to some chemicals, gasoline burns slowly. However, when this same gasoline is broken up into a fine spray and mixed with the right amount of air, it becomes very explosive and produces great heat and power.

Carburetors

The carburetor of a small engine must be able to take liquid gasoline and break it up into a fine mist. It must mix the mist with the exact amount of air needed for complete combustion in the engine cylinder. It must do this at all operating speeds from idle to wide-open throttle, and at all operating temperatures from cold start to full operating. The correct mixture is *one part* of gasoline, by mass, to about *fifteen parts* of air.

Look at the carburetor closely. To do all the things described above, the carburetor must be divided into four separate systems of fuel and air passages and valves. These are:

(a) The supply system
(b) The high speed system
(c) The choke system
(d) The idle speed system

Be careful: Never work around gasoline or gas-soaked rags if there is danger of fire. Do not smoke, light matches, or strike sparks.

Be careful: Do not leave gasoline-soaked rags around in a pile; a fire could result.

Governor: a speed control for an engine.

Many small engines are controlled at a particular operating speed by a governor and have no idle speed system in their carburetors. Governors are described in the next chapter.

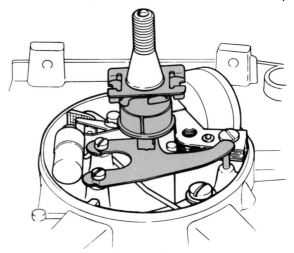

Mechanical governor

THE SUPPLY SYSTEM

Gravity: the natural force that pulls everything down towards the centre of the earth.

Carburetors for use on small engines are described by the method by which they draw fuel from the fuel tank. The drawings below show gravity feed carburetors. Gravity feed carburetors have their fuel tank mounted above them. The gasoline runs down to a small container on the carburetor called the float bowl.

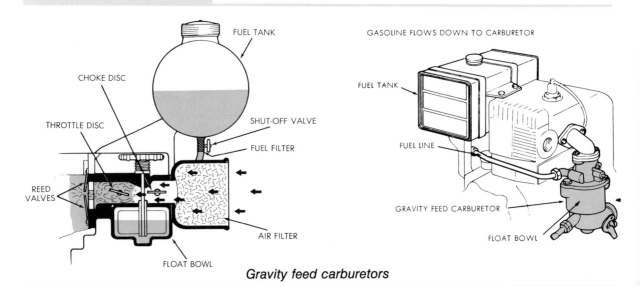

Gravity feed carburetors

The level of fuel in the bowl is controlled by a small float connected to a needle valve. When the float rises it closes the needle valve, and stops the flow of fuel from the tank.

The float and needle valve work together to keep the right amount of gasoline in the float bowl at all times. The main fuel jet draws fuel from the float bowl.

Be careful: Gasoline fumes are hazardous to breathe. Work with good ventilation.

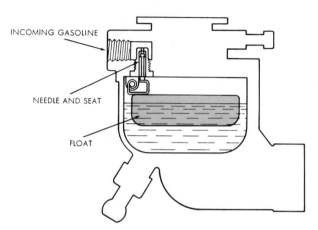

Cutaway of float chamber and needle assembly

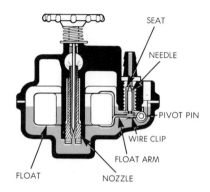

Cutaway of gravity feed carburetor

Be careful: Gasoline fumes are explosive. Gasoline should be stored in a sturdy, sealed gasoline can and kept outside.

The carburetors used on the engines that power machines such as chain saws must be able to work in any position. They need a diaphragm fuel supply system that will not spill when the carburetor is tipped. This style of carburetor is called a diaphragm carburetor. The diaphragm and its spring take the place of a float to control the supply of gasoline to the carburetor.

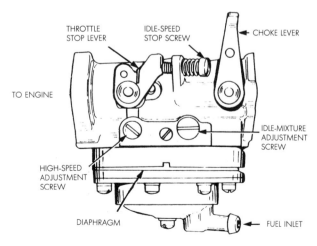

A gravity fed diaphragm carburetor

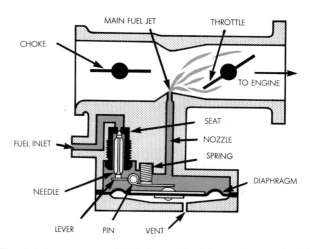

The intake vacuum that draws fuel from the main jet also pulls the diaphragm against spring pressure and opens the inlet needle.

Suction: a force that causes a gas or liquid to move from an area of high or normal air pressure to an area of low air pressure.

Jet: a tube with a small opening to allow a liquid to rush through.

Another type of small engine carburetor is the suction feed carburetor. It is fastened to the top of the fuel tank. The main fuel jet hangs down into the fuel tank, so that no float bowl is needed.

Carburetors of the suction feed style must be adjusted while the tank is half full. Carburetors of this type tend to provide an over-rich fuel/air mixture with a full tank, and a lean mixture when the fuel level is low. The engine first gets too much gasoline and later "starves".

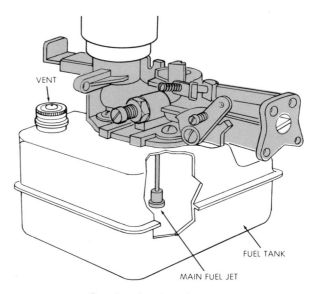

Suction feed carburetor

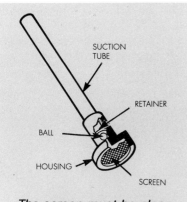

The screen must be clean and the check ball free to move.

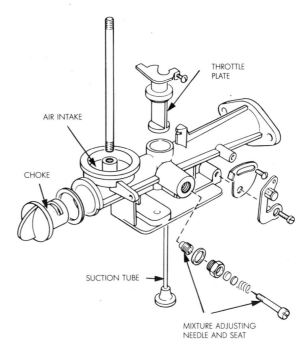

Exploded view of suction feed carburetor

An improvement on this carburetor uses a built-in diaphragm fuel pump operated by intake vacuum. The pump keeps a small cup in the fuel tank full of gasoline. The carburetor draws fuel from the cup so it is not affected by the level of gasoline in the tank. Excess fuel pumped into the cup spills over into the tank.

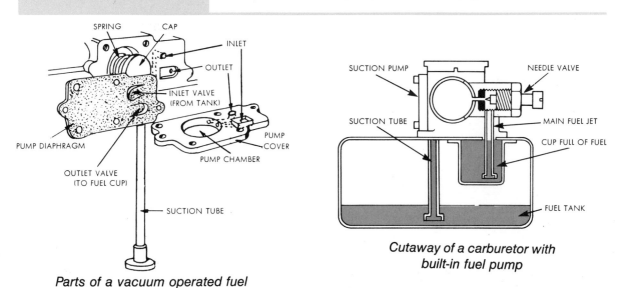

Parts of a vacuum operated fuel pump on the side of a carburetor

Cutaway of a carburetor with built-in fuel pump

Some of the larger engines have a small fuel pump to supply gasoline to the carburetor float bowl. The fuel tank does not have to be above the carburetor in this case. The diaphragm of the pump is moved by a lever resting on a cam on either the crankshaft or camshaft of the engine.

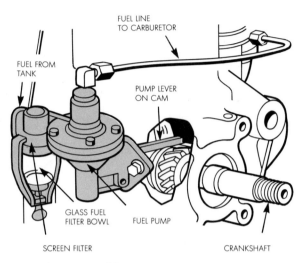

A cam and lever operated fuel pump

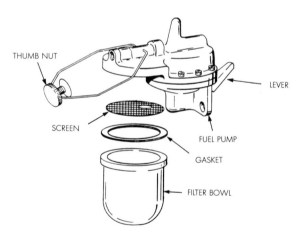

Details of a fuel filter as used on a lever operated fuel pump

THE HIGH SPEED SYSTEM

When the piston is moving down on the intake stroke, it sucks both gasoline and air into the cylinder through the carburetor. If the fuel were allowed to pour directly into the throat of the carburetor, the engine would always be flooded with too much gasoline. This is why all carburetors draw the fuel up from the float bowl or tank through a nozzle called the main fuel jet.

The faster the air is sucked past the main fuel jet, the more gasoline will be drawn from the supply. You will notice from the drawings in this chapter that the main fuel jet enters the carburetor throat at a narrow spot called the venturi. This narrow opening causes the air to speed up past the fuel jet, just as wind moves faster through a narrow alley between two buildings.

As the air speeds up through the venturi, an area of low air pressure is created around the main fuel jet. This makes the gasoline flow up the jet to get to the low pressure area. When the gasoline leaves the jet, the rushing air breaks the liquid into a fine spray in the carburetor throat.

The float bowl must have an air vent to let normal air pressure act on the fuel.

The flow of gasoline is adjusted by turning a screw called the

Venturi: the narrow spot in a carburetor that causes a low air pressure area around the fuel jet.

Vent: a hole that allows air to move in or out of a container

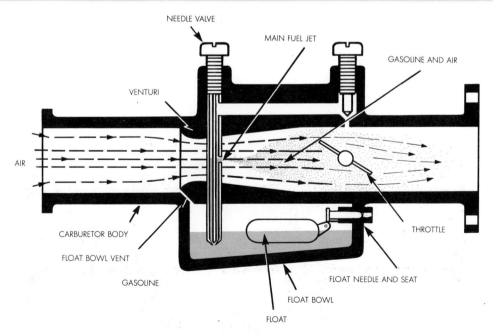

Cutaway of carburetor showing the high speed system in use

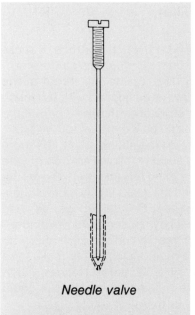

Needle valve

Throttle: a valve that controls the amount of fuel and air entering the cylinder of an engine.

r/min: revolutions per minute.

needle valve in or out of the main jet. With an engine running at the usual operating speed, turn this needle valve screw in slowly until the engine stalls, and then turn the screw back about half a turn. This is the right place for it to be.

A round disc of metal, called the throttle, is mounted on a shaft after the venturi to open or close off the throat of the carburetor. By opening or closing the throttle, the amount of fuel/air mixture that gets to the cylinder can be controlled, making the engine go faster or slower.

THE IDLE CIRCUIT

When the throttle closes off the carburetor throat, none of the fuel/air mixture can get to the cylinder from the high speed system. To allow the engine to run at a slow idle speed when the throttle is almost closed, air and fuel are sucked through a small passage to a jet in the carburetor throat. This jet is past the edge of the almost closed throttle.

You can adjust the mixture of fuel and air for the smoothest idle. Turn the idle valve adjustment screw in slowly until the engine stalls, then back the screw out about half a turn.

The idle speed can be set to the desired r/min by turning a screw on the throttle shaft. When the screw is turned in against a stop, the throttle is held open slightly to allow some air to slip by the throttle. The idle mixture adjustment should then be changed to give the smoothest idle at the new speed.

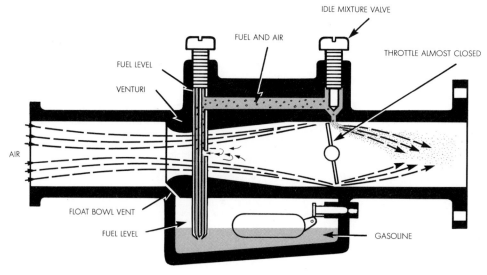

The idle speed circuit

Be careful: Gasoline fumes are explosive. Do not smoke while filling a fuel tank.

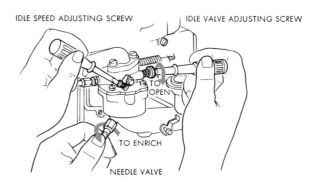

Adjusting the carburetor

SLIDE THROTTLE CARBURETORS

Many carburetors used on snowmobiles, motorcycles and ultra light aircraft have slide throttles which actually change the size of the venturi as they open and close. This feature plus its adjustable needle valve allows more accurate mixture control at all speeds.

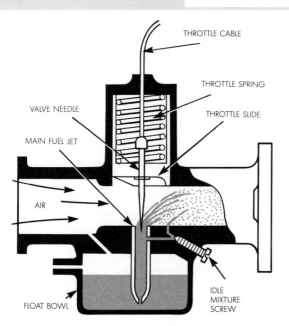

The high speed circuit of a slide throttle carburetor. The throttle is in the wide open position.

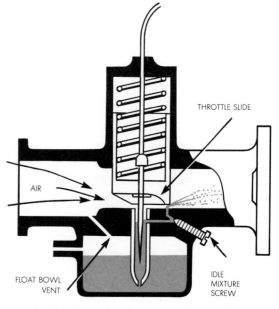

A slide throttle closed to idle position. The bottom of the throttle slide is shaped to position the smallest venturi passage above the idle jet.

THE CHOKE CIRCUIT

A cold engine needs a rich mixture in order to start and run for the first few minutes. A rich mixture is one that has more fuel and less air than a normal mixture. The choke valve, placed in the carburetor throat before the venturi, cuts down on the amount of air entering the carburetor and causes more gasoline to be sucked from the main fuel jet. As you can see, the choke valve does not cut off all the air to the carburetor. It has a hole or notch in it to let some air through. When the choke valve is closed, fuel and air are also drawn through the idle circuit.

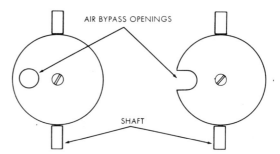

Example of choke valves

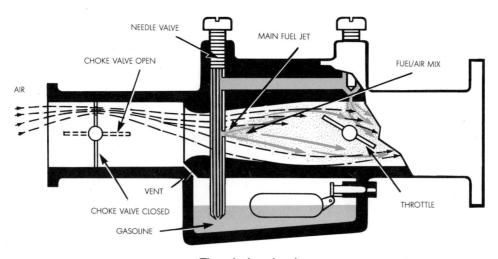

The choke circuit

The carburetors on some small engines have automatic chokes that are held closed by a light spring when the engine is stopped or is cold. The drawing shows a choke plate that is attached to a diaphragm. A small passage connects the diaphragm housing to the intake manifold. When the engine starts, vacuum in the intake manifold pulls on the diaphragm and opens the choke. This type of automatic choke tends to behave like a governor. Another type has the choke lever attached to a thermostat and as the engine temperature increases, the thermostat gradually opens the choke. The thermostat must be fastened to the cylinder wall of the engine and adjusted to open the choke fully at a certain temperature.

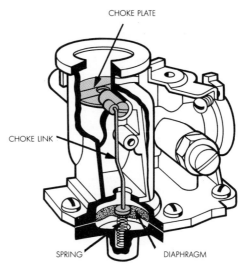

A vacuum operated automatic choke

PRIMERS

Instead of a choke valve, some carburetors use a primer to make a rich starting mixture. The primer lifts or pushes a quantity of gasoline into the carburetor throat. A choke reduces the amount of air mixing with the fuel. A primer increases the amount of fuel mixing with the air.

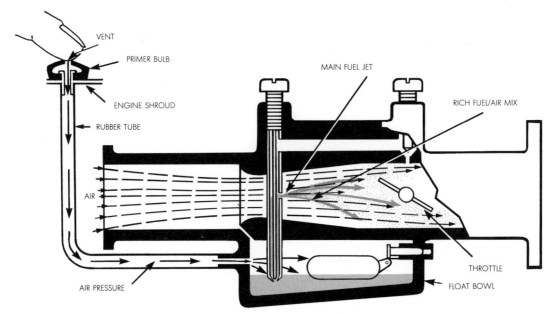

Finger pressure on the rubber primer bulb causes air pressure on the fuel in the float bowl and pushes gasoline through the main fuel jet.

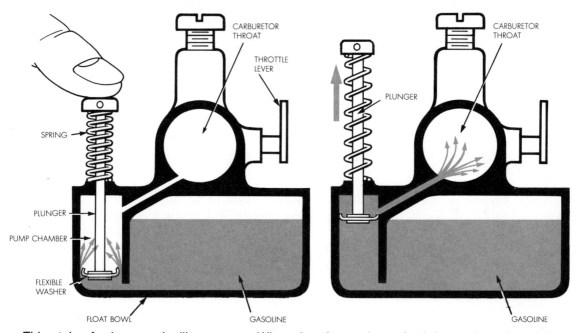

This style of primer works like a pump. When the plunger is pushed down, the edge of the cup-shaped washer flexes and lets gasoline into the pump chamber. When finger pressure is removed, the spring lifts the plunger and gasoline is pumped into the carburetor throat.

CARBURETOR AIR CLEANERS

The biggest enemy of both the carburetor and the engine is dirt. Dirt in the gasoline slowly plugs the fuel jets. Dirt in the air can cause scratched and worn piston rings and cylinder walls. When dirt gets mixed with the oil, it causes the bearings to wear rapidly. An engine that is used in dirty, dusty conditions will have a very short life if the owner forgets regular air cleaner service and oil changes, and does not use clean gasoline from a clean container.

Even a small, single cylinder engine needs large amounts of clean air. The makers install one of three types of air cleaners on each carburetor, to make sure the air is clean when it reaches the engine. The air cleaners filter out dirt from the air. This dirt gradually plugs up the air cleaner and cuts off the flow of air to the carburetor. The engine begins to act as though the choke is closed all the time because it cannot get enough air. It is then time to clean or replace the filter.

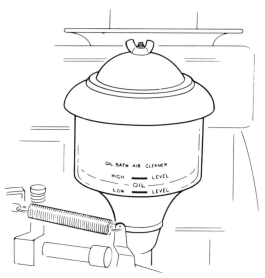

Oil bath air cleaner

The drawing above shows an **oil bath** air cleaner. Air passing through this type of cleaner must flow across the surface of an oil sump and then through metal mesh to the carburetor throat. Bits of dirt and dust become trapped in the oil and the mesh and should be cleaned out regularly. Pour out the old oil and clean the oil bowl with a wiping cloth. Wash the mesh in solvent and let it drain dry. Refill the bowl with oil to the oil level mark, and fasten the cleaner to the carburetor.

Filter: a special paper, cloth, metal mesh or wire screen with very small openings in it. Air can get through the openings but dirt specks are too big.

Safety First: Be sure to dispose of used oil properly. Always keep your workshop free of slippery floors or tools.

Mesh: the threads or fine wire of a net or screen.

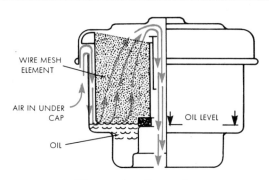

*Air passing through an
oil bath air cleaner*

Refill bowl to oil level mark.

Solvent: a liquid, such as
varsol, used as a cleaner.

Oil wetted air cleaners trap dirt in an element of foam rubber,
wire mesh or crumpled foil that has been wetted with a few drops
of oil. Wash the element in solvent regularly and apply a few
drops of clean oil.

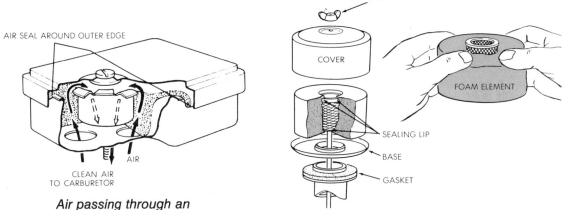

*Air passing through an
oil wetted air cleaner*

Parts of an oil wetted air cleaner

Dry element air cleaners are the newest type of air cleaner
available. The element is made of folded paper, enclosed in a
screen. All air to the carburetor must pass through the paper
element. When the element gets dirty it can be thrown away
and replaced with a new one at little cost. It is possible to clean
some of the dirt out by tapping the element on a hard flat surface,
as shown.

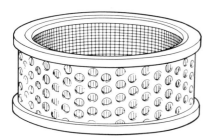

Dry element air cleaner

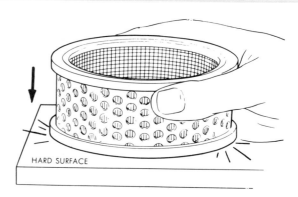

HARD SURFACE

Cleaning a dry element air cleaner

Pressurized Fuel Tanks

In order to use outboard boat engines for long cruises, a large fuel tank is used. This tank is separate from the engine and sits on the bottom of the boat. Either crankcase pressure or vacuum suction is used to move fuel from the tank to the carburetor.

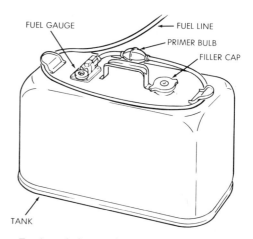

FUEL GAUGE   FUEL LINE
PRIMER BULB
FILLER CAP
TANK

Fuel tank for outboard boat engines

Be careful: When filling a gasoline can or tank, touch the fuel nozzle to the tank first to let any static electricity flow to ground. Then hold the nozzle against one side of the filler neck while filling the container.

For the fuel to flow from the tank to the carburetor, some of the crankcase pressure is used to push on the fuel in the tank and force it through the fuel line to the float bowl. You can see how this works in the picture on the next page.

A small reed valve on the crankcase opens on the *down* stroke of the piston and closes on the *up* stroke. The fuel tank must be air tight. When the carburetor fuel bowl is full and the float has closed the needle against its seat, any extra tank pressure escapes through a relief valve.

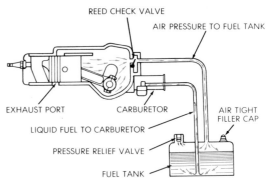

Pressure fuel system

Fuel Pumps

Some of the larger outboard engines use a small suction pump to lift fuel from the tank and push it into the carburetor fuel bowl. A hand-operated rubber squeeze bulb in the fuel line must be used to supply the carburetor with fuel for starting. A rubber tube connects the fuel pump to the crankcase of the engine.

When the piston moves up in the cylinder, the crankcase vacuum pulls on the rubber pump diaphragm. This causes a small poppet valve to open, and fuel is drawn into the fuel pump.

Diaphragm: a flat disc of cloth and rubber in a fuel pump. It separates the fuel tank side of the pump from the engine side.

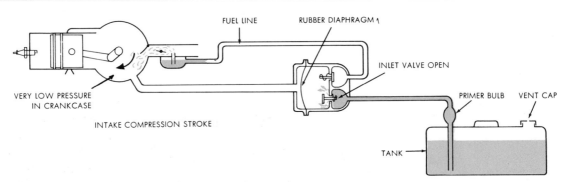

Fuel pump drawing fuel from tank

When the engine piston moves down in the cylinder, crankcase pressure pushes on the pump diaphragm. The intake poppet valve closes, and the fuel is pushed out of the pump through a second poppet valve to the carburetor.

This system must have an air vent in the fuel tank.

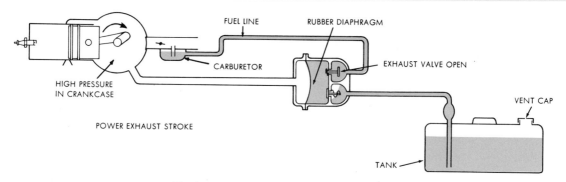

FUEL LINE   RUBBER DIAPHRAGM

EXHAUST VALVE OPEN

CARBURETOR

HIGH PRESSURE
IN CRANKCASE

VENT CAP

POWER EXHAUST STROKE

TANK

Fuel pump pushing fuel to carburetor

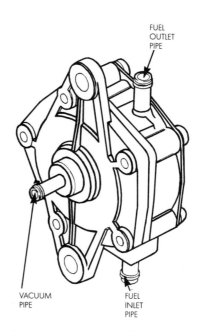

FUEL
OUTLET
PIPE

VACUUM
PIPE

FUEL
INLET
PIPE

A vacuum operated fuel pump

Things to Do

1. Take apart a gravity feed carburetor and locate the following parts:

   (a) float
   (b) float bowl vent
   (c) float needle and seat
   (d) main fuel jet
   (e) venturi

   (f) needle valve
   (g) throttle
   (h) choke
   (i) idle jet
   (j) idle mixture screw

   Clean the parts carefully and re-assemble the carburetor.

2. Look at a suction feed carburetor and list the main parts. Compare your list with the gravity feed carburetor parts list.

3. Find examples of the three styles of carburetor air cleaners. Follow the instructions in this chapter to clean each style.

4. Start a small engine and use a screwdriver to adjust the idle speed and mixture screws for the best engine performance at idle.

5. With an engine running at its usual operating speed, adjust the needle valve as described in this chapter.

6. List the parts of a pressure tank fuel system, and a pump fuel system. Compare the lists.

A light motorcycle for use on roads and highways

CHAPTER 8

ENGINE SPEED GOVERNORS

Watch for These Words

vane
counterbalances
centrifugal

How to Use These Words

1. The force of air pushing against a *vane* can be used to control the carburetor throttle.
2. In mechanical governors, *counterbalances* pull against a spring.
3. The counterbalances are often *centrifugal* to the crankshaft.

Look for Answers to These Questions

1. Name two types of engine speed governors.
2. State in your own words the purpose of governors on a small engine.
3. When the governor spring is tightened, what effect does it have on engine speed?
4. Describe the operation of one type of engine governor.
5. What kind of force causes the counterbalances to swing away from a spinning shaft?

Engine Speed Governors

Most small engines are used to power machines that do both light and heavy work. Lawnmowers are a good example. They move from short, easy cutting into long tough grass again and again. Sudden heavy loads such as this would normally cause the engine to slow down or stop entirely. The governor is an automatic device that opens the throttle for more power when the work load gets heavy, and closes the throttle when the load is light. In this way the engine speed changes very little, no matter what the load.

The air vane governor and the mechanical governor are the two types used on small engines.

Air vane governor

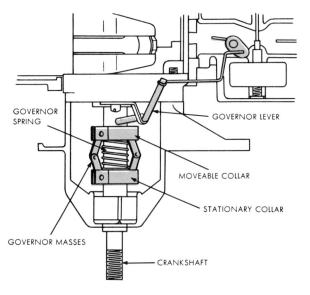

Mechanical governor

THE AIR VANE GOVERNOR

Vane: a flat metal or plastic surface fastened to a shaft, and moved by air or wind.

This type of speed governor uses the force of air from the fly-wheel fan to push against a light, flat piece of metal or plastic, called the air vane. The air vane is linked to the throttle, which is held open by a spring. The tension of the spring is often adjustable, to allow the operator to change engine speed.

When the engine starts, air is blown against the air vane. The vane moves and pulls on the spring. This closes the throttle to the desired operating speed. When the load gets heavy and

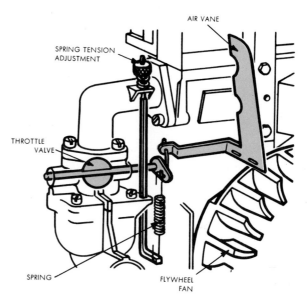

Engine not running — throttle open

the flywheel begins to slow down, less air strikes the air vane and the spring pulls the throttle open until the engine speed picks up again.

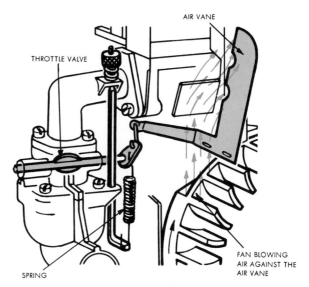

Engine running — throttle partly closed

Cutaway engines are helpful, but if none is available, the air vane governor can be seen by removing the engine cooling shroud.

A motor generator must run at a steady governed speed.

Counterbalance: a mass used to balance a force.

Centrifugal: moving in a direction away from centre.

THE MECHANICAL GOVERNOR

The mechanical governor is sometimes called the counter-balance governor. It uses a set of hinged masses to pull against the pull of the throttle spring. The masses are fastened to the crankshaft, camshaft, or sometimes a separately driven shaft. When the engine is running, the shaft spins and the masses tend to fly out, away from the centre of the shaft. This pull away from the shaft is known as centrifugal force.

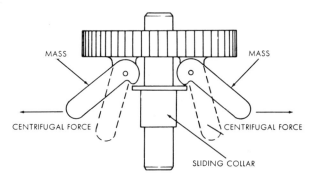

Centrifugal force acting on the governor counterbalances

As the masses swing out, away from the shaft, they move a lever that is linked to the throttle. This closes the throttle as far as the governor spring will allow, and the engine then runs at the desired speed. When a heavy operating load begins to slow the engine speed, the centrifugal force decreases, the counterbalances swing in slightly, and the spring opens the throttle for more power. As the load becomes lighter, the engine speed increases until the counterbalances return the throttle to its normal operating position. A governor that is in good condition and working properly will react quickly. This means there will be very slight speed drops and increases as the work load changes.

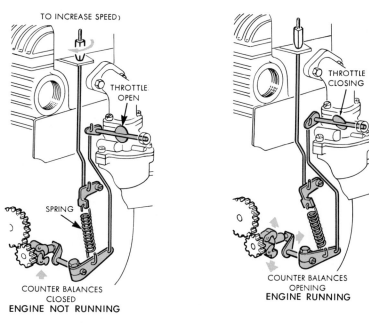

Operation of mechanical governor

Some mechanical governors have the counterbalance unit mounted inside a removable housing, as shown below. On other models you must remove the flywheel or the crankcase cover.

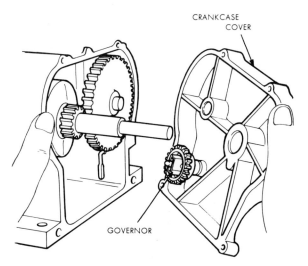

Removing the crankcase cover

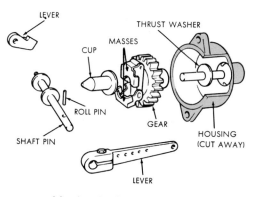

Mechanical governor in a removable housing

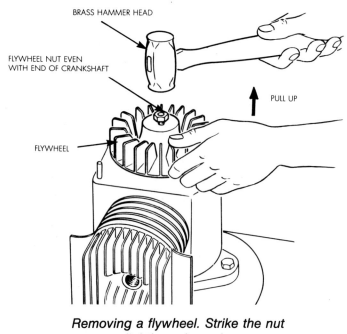

BRASS HAMMER HEAD

FLYWHEEL NUT EVEN WITH END OF CRANKSHAFT

FLYWHEEL

PULL UP

Removing a flywheel. Strike the nut lightly and evenly.

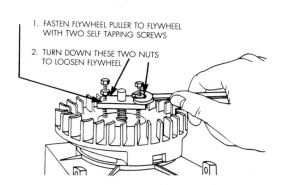

1. FASTEN FLYWHEEL PULLER TO FLYWHEEL WITH TWO SELF TAPPING SCREWS

2. TURN DOWN THESE TWO NUTS TO LOOSEN FLYWHEEL

Use a flywheel puller when the repair manual suggests it. Follow the directions carefully.

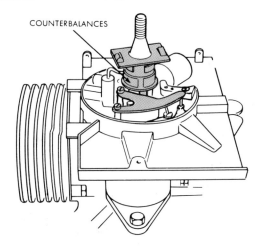

COUNTERBALANCES

Position of governor under the flywheel

Things to Do

1. Closely examine examples of both types of speed governors.

2. With an engine operating, adjust the governor spring tension as shown, and note the change in engine speed.

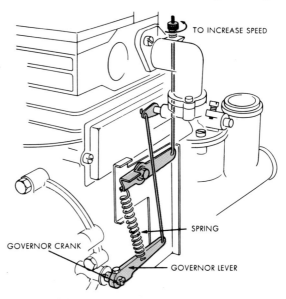

Adjusting governor spring tension

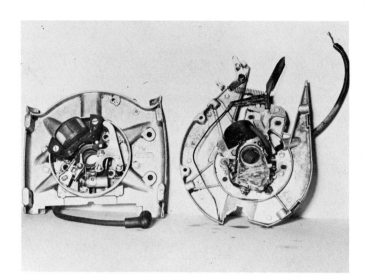

CHAPTER 9

IGNITION SYSTEMS

Watch for These Words

stationary	*diode*	*ground*
magnet	*rectifier*	*transistors*
generate	*alternating current*	*silicon*
lodestone	*direct current*	*volt*
condenser	*insulator*	*alloy*
tungsten	*bushing*	*current*

How to Use These Words

1. *Stationary* engines are often used by industry to power machinery.

2. A moving *magnet* can be used to *generate* electricity in a coil of wire.

3. Early man found that a *lodestone* would attract and hold iron objects.

4. A *condenser* is used to protect the *tungsten* breaker points from electrical damage.

5. A *diode* may be used as a *rectifier* to change *alternating current* to *direct current.*

6. Porcelain is a good electrical *insulator.*

7. An insulating *bushing* is used to keep one of the breaker points free of *ground.*

8. Some *transistors* are made from *silicon.*

9. The cells of a storage battery will each produce electricity at two *volts.*

130

10. Permanent magnets are made of a special *alloy*.

11. A small, positive *current* will open the gate of an SCR (silicon controlled rectifier).

Find the Answers to These Questions

1. What is a magneto?
2. Name four styles of magnetos.
3. Name the parts of a primary circuit of a magneto.
4. Name the parts of a secondary circuit.
5. When is an electrical circuit complete?
6. Why do some small engines have battery ignition systems?
7. What part of a magneto does a battery replace in an ignition system?
8. How many storage cells are there in a 12-volt battery?

The Magneto

Magneto ignition systems are used on engines where no electricity must be supplied for starters and lights. Steady electrical current for starters and lights must be supplied by a storage battery. The ignition systems for engines with this equipment may also be battery powered.

The magneto is a device designed to use the magnetic field of force that exists around a permanent magnet. This force field is used to generate electricity in a coil of wire. The most commonly used magneto for small engines has a moving magnet and a stationary coil. The magnet is part of the flywheel or of a rotor driven by the crankshaft.

Stationary: fixed in a certain position.

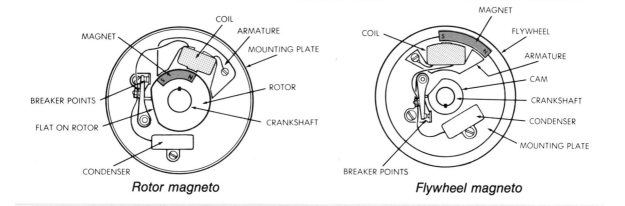

Rotor magneto   Flywheel magneto

Other styles of magnetos are the shuttle wound magneto and the rotary inductor magneto. The shuttle wound magneto has a revolving coil and stationary magnet. The rotary inductor magneto has a stationary coil and magnet. It uses a rotor to start and stop the magnetic field through the coil.

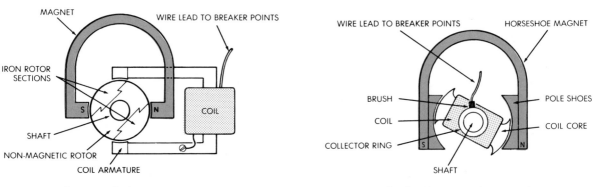

A rotary inductor magneto   *A shuttle wound magneto*

All magneto ignition systems have two separate electrical circuits. These are the primary or generating circuit and the secondary or step-up circuit.

THE PRIMARY CIRCUIT

The primary (first) circuit includes the primary winding of the ignition coil, the breaker points, and a condenser. The breaker points are opened by a cam and closed by a strong spring.

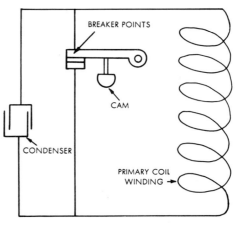

The primary circuit, with points closed

THE SECONDARY CIRCUIT

Volt: a unit of electrical pressure.

This high voltage circuit includes the secondary winding of the coil, the high voltage lead, and the spark plug.

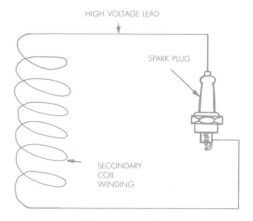

Parts of the secondary circuit

Current: the flow of electrons through a conductor, measured in amperes.

An electric circuit is not complete unless there is a continuous path for the electrical current to run through. No current can flow in the primary circuit when the breaker points are open. No current can flow in the secondary circuit unless enough voltage can be produced to push the current across the spark plug gap. The spark gap has a very high resistance to current flow.

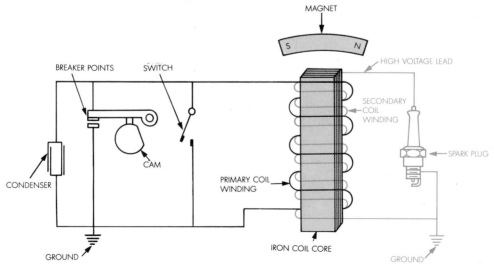

A magneto ignition system

Magnet: a piece of metal which has a force field around it that attracts iron.

When a spark occurs between the spark plug electrodes, the secondary circuit is complete.

A permanent magnet and a soft iron core for the ignition coil windings are the only other parts of the magneto ignition system.

A switch in the primary circuit may be used to stop the engine by providing a short circuit to ground. You should notice that in all ignition systems the word 'ground' means the crankcase or cylinder block of the engine. All parts of both the secondary and primary circuits have one side fastened to ground.

BATTERY IGNITION

Be careful: Battery acid is dangerous. If spilled on any part of the body, wash with lots of water right away.

Battery ignition is often used on small engines that are equipped with electric starters and are used in machines such as boats, snowmobiles, or large garden tractors, that have electric lights.

The battery takes the place of the rotating magnet of a magneto and supplies electric current to the primary winding of the ignition coil.

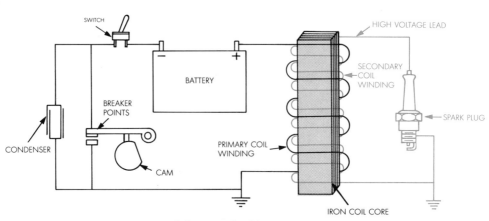

A battery ignition system

Electrolyte: a liquid that will conduct electricity. It is a mixture of water and sulphuric acid in a storage battery.

Batteries act like containers for electricity and are often called storage batteries.

Some rechargeable dry cell batteries are used with small engines but the automotive style wet cell battery is common. The drawing shows a battery made up of six cells connected together and held in a case. Such a battery will produce an electrical current at 12 volts when filled with the correct water and acid electrolyte. One terminal post is labelled negative and the other is positive. Electricity always flows through a circuit from negative to positive. It is important to connect the wire cables to the correct battery posts.

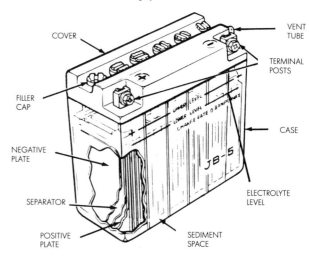

A cutaway view of a 12-volt battery

Be careful: Batteries give off an explosive gas. There should be no smoking, no flames, and no sparks near them at any time.

Electricity and Magnetism

Find the Answers to These Questions

1. What is a magnet?
2. In what direction do magnetic lines of force travel?
3. Do magnetic lines of force travel more easily through air, or through iron?
4. What happens in a coil of wire when magnetic lines of force pass quickly through it?
5. How can a coil of wire be made to act like a magnet?
6. Why does the magneto secondary coil have many more turns of wire than the primary coil?

THE MAGNET

The first magnets discovered by man were pieces of iron-bearing rock that had the ability to attract and hold other pieces of iron. When allowed to move freely, these lodestones, as they were called, turned so that one end always pointed toward the north. Lodestones are very weak when compared with modern man-

Lodestone: a natural magnet.

Alloy: a mixture of two or more kinds of metal.

made magnets, but they were used as compasses by early sea captains.

The magnets used in flywheel and rotor magnetos are made of special steel alloys. They hold their magnetism over such a long period of time that they are called permanent magnets. The drawing shows a permanent bar magnet. The light lines around the magnet represent the lines of force making up the field of magnetism. Note that this magnetic field is strongest at the poles of the magnet and that the lines of force always travel from the North pole toward the South pole.

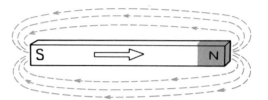

Permanent bar magnet

Lines of magnetic force cannot be seen around an actual magnet but their effect can certainly be felt. Here is an experiment to show the magnetic field around a magnet.

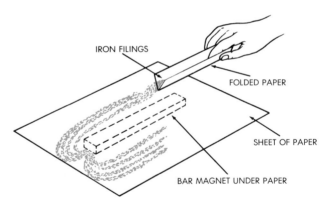

Lines of force around a bar magnet

ELECTRICITY FROM A MAGNET

Magnetic lines of force travel much more easily through iron than through air. When a permanent magnet passes near a bar of iron, its invisible lines of force pass from the North pole to the South pole through the iron.

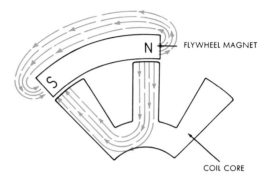

Magnetic lines of force passing through iron

Generate: to produce electricity.

When the direction of magnetism through an iron core is quickly reversed, electricity will be generated in a coil of wire around the core.

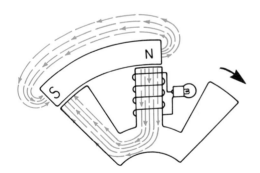

Magnetic lines of force travelling down the centre leg of a coil core

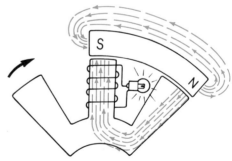

Electricity is generated by suddenly changing the direction of the lines of force through the coil.

Safety Note: Do NOT experiment with coils of wire attached to shop or house electrical wall outlets. This is a very dangerous act.

Experiment with three to six volt, dry or wet cell batteries. Connect only one end of the coil to a battery post. You will see good results by tapping the other coil wire on the other post.

A sensitive ammeter will be more likely to show current flow than the small bulbs shown in these drawings.

When electricity flows through a coil of wire, a field of magnetism builds up around the coil.

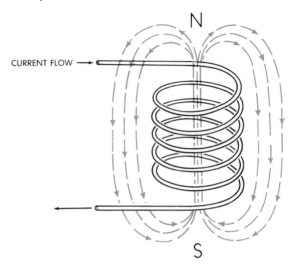

A magnetic field forms around a coil of wire.

When the magnetic field around a coil quickly increases, decreases, or changes direction, electricity will flow in a nearby coil of wire.

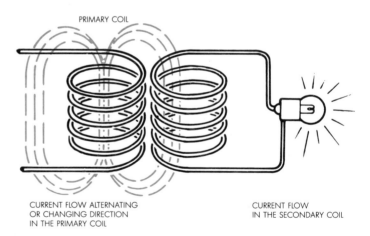

CURRENT FLOW ALTERNATING OR CHANGING DIRECTION IN THE PRIMARY COIL

CURRENT FLOW IN THE SECONDARY COIL

When the secondary coil of wire has many more turns of wire than the primary coil, electricity in the secondary coil will flow at a much higher voltage.

A 115-volt alternating current generator powered by a small four stroke cycle engine

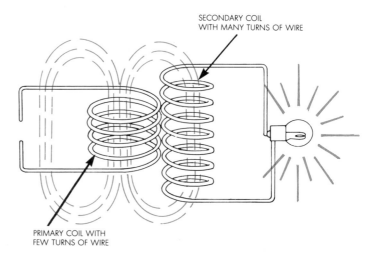

SECONDARY COIL WITH MANY TURNS OF WIRE

PRIMARY COIL WITH FEW TURNS OF WIRE

Low voltage primary current is changed to high voltage secondary current.

Parts of a Magneto

THE IGNITION COIL

The ignition coil is actually two coils of wire wrapped around the same iron core. This core is not solid but made up of thin sheets of soft iron or steel. The winding next to the core is made up of a small number of turns of *heavy* varnished wire. This is the primary winding. Around this are wound several thousand turns of *very fine* varnished wire. This is the secondary winding. The varnish prevents the wires from touching each other and short-circuiting the coil. A sudden flow of electricity in the primary winding, at a low voltage, will cause electricity to flow in the secondary winding at a much greater voltage, due to the greater number of turns of wire.

The magneto ignition coil must be able to produce between

Short-circuit: to make a new, shorter path for electricity. The original circuit no longer works.

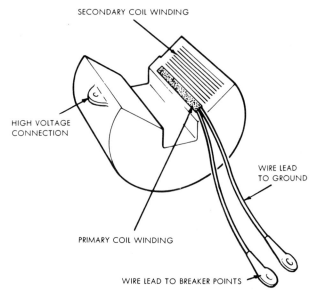

SECONDARY COIL WINDING

HIGH VOLTAGE CONNECTION

WIRE LEAD TO GROUND

PRIMARY COIL WINDING

WIRE LEAD TO BREAKER POINTS

A cutaway drawing of an ignition coil

15 000 and 30 000 V of electrical pressure in order to cause a spark of electricity to arc between the spark plug electrodes.

The illustrations below show two types of ignition coils used on small engines.

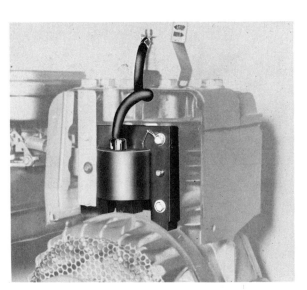

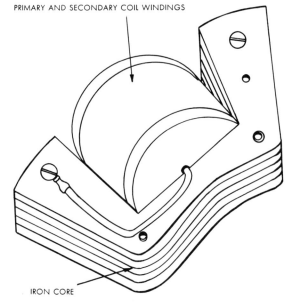

PRIMARY AND SECONDARY COIL WINDINGS

IRON CORE

Two styles of magneto ignition coils

The Breaker Points and Condenser

Find the Answers to These Questions

1. What is the purpose of the breaker points in a magneto?
2. What metal is used to make the contact points?
3. What part of the engine causes the breaker points to open?
4. Name the tool used to measure breaker point gap.
5. Why is a condenser needed in the primary circuit?

BREAKER POINTS

The breaker points are an automatic switch connected in the primary circuit of the magneto. They are operated by a cam on the crankshaft. When the points are closed, the primary circuit is complete and electrical current can flow. When the breaker points open, the primary circuit is broken and current flow quickly stops.

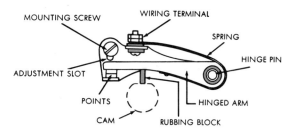

A set of breaker points. Note the insulating bushings and rubbing block shown in colour.

Bushing: a friction type of shaft bearing.

Ground: an electrical connection or contact to the cylinder block.

Tungsten: a hard, white metal that is a very good conductor of electricity.

One contact arm is fastened to the mounting plate, while the other is held against the cam by a strong spring. The movable arm pivots on an insulating bushing and is otherwise completely kept from touching metal parts of the magneto. Care must be taken to avoid accidental grounding of this arm when attaching the primary coil lead or when adjusting the opening between the points.

The contacts are usually made of tungsten and must be very carefully adjusted to open to the engine manufacturer's specified gap. The next drawing shows another style of breaker points.

The movable contact is operated by an insulated plunger that is lifted by the cam. This cam may be a separate part keyed to the crankshaft, or just a machined area on the shaft itself.

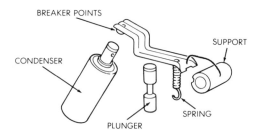

Plunger operated points

Be careful: Feeler gauges are precision tools. They must not be bent, or put away when they are not clean.

A flat feeler gauge and screwdriver are used to adjust the breaker point gap. The cam must be in position to hold the points open for this adjustment.

1. Turn the crankshaft until the ignition cam holds the breaker points open fully.
2. Loosen the breaker mounting screw slightly. If there are two mounting screws, loosen both of them.
3. Place a feeler gauge of the correct thickness between the contacts. Be careful to hold the gauge parallel to the faces of the contacts.
4. Move the loosened arm until both contacts just touch the sides of the feeler gauge. A slight drag can be felt when the gauge is moved back and forth.
5. Tighten the breaker mounting screw and try the feeler gauge between the contacts again to make sure the setting has not changed.

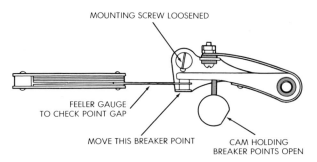

Adjusting breaker point gap

THE CONDENSER

The condenser is connected in the primary circuit of the magneto to prevent electricity from jumping across the breaker points as they open. This quickly stops current flow in the primary circuit and prevents burning or pitting of the breaker points. The simple construction of a condenser is shown here.

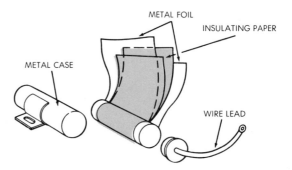

Condenser construction

Two sheets of metal foil, separated by sheets of insulating paper, are rolled tightly together and placed in a metal can. One sheet of foil is fastened to the can, and the other is connected by a wire lead to the breaker points.

When a condenser is not working properly, the breaker points are soon damaged by burning and pitting, caused by electrical sparks arcing between them. The only repair for this kind of damage is to replace the breaker points and the condenser.

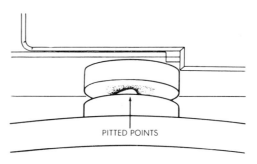

Damage to breaker points

A completely grounded condenser is often the cause of a no-spark condition.

Condenser: an electrical device used in the primary circuit. It has the ability to collect and hold electricity.

Be careful: A large condenser can store electricity at high voltage. You can get a strong electrical shock when handling one.

The Spark Plug

Find the Answers to These Questions

1. List some of the causes of spark plug failure.
2. When is a spark plug unfit to be re-used in an engine?
3. What tool is used to measure and adjust a spark plug gap?
4. Why are spark plugs made in several different heat ranges?
5. What is spark plug reach?
6. What problems could be caused by installing a spark plug with (a) short reach? (b) long reach?

The spark plug is threaded through the cylinder head. Its electrodes project into the combustion chamber. When the piston reaches the top of the compression stroke, a spark jumps between the electrodes of the spark plug. This ignites the fuel/air charge and forces the piston down on the power stroke.

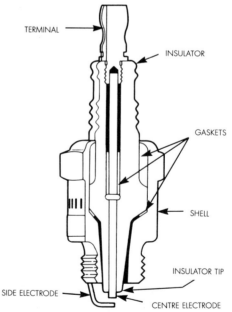

A cutaway drawing showing the parts of a spark plug

Insulator: a type of material that does not conduct electricity.

Be careful: Bend only the side electrode to adjust the spark gap.

The heavy high voltage wire from the secondary winding of the ignition coil connects to the cap on the centre electrode of the spark plug. This electrode passes through a ceramic insulator and does not touch any of the metal parts of the spark plug.

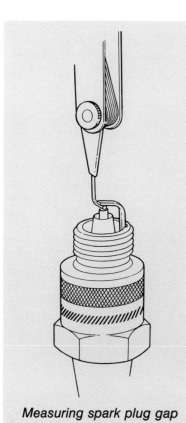

Measuring spark plug gap

The other electrode extends from the threaded shell of the spark plug to a position near the centre electrode. It is called the side electrode. The gap between the electrodes is called the spark gap. The gap can be measured and adjusted with a wire spark gap gauge as shown. The correct spark gap is always listed in the engine manual.

The condition of the spark plug is very important. When the electrodes become worn or burned, the gap may be so wide that the magneto cannot force an electrical spark to jump between them. A badly adjusted carburetor can cause a thick coating of carbon on the insulator and electrodes. Worn piston rings allow oil into the cylinder. When it burns, an oily carbon will be left in the cylinder and on the spark plug. Too much oil mixed with the fuel in two stroke cycle engines will do the same thing. The carbon conducts electric current away from the electrode gap. When this happens, no spark occurs. With any of these conditions, the engine will not start. It is wise to inspect spark plugs regularly.

1. To inspect the spark plug, remove the high voltage wire from the terminal nut and loosen the spark plug a few turns. Use a spark plug socket wrench of the correct size.

2. Wipe or air blast all dirt away from around the spark plug, so that nothing will fall into the cylinder when the plug is removed. A small paint brush does a good job of dirt removal when compressed air is not available.

Be careful: If you get dirt in the cylinder, it can damage the engine badly.

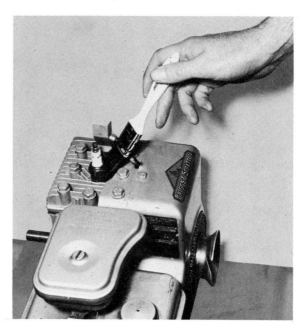

Clean cylinder head

3. Remove the spark plug and clean it thoroughly in a spark plug cleaning machine. Abrasive blast for about six seconds, then air blast. Throw away plugs with cracked insulators or badly worn electrodes. If the spark plug appears to be in good condition, be very careful to remove all the sand from the shell and insulator. A few bits of sand in the cylinder of an engine will quickly wear grooves or scratches in the cylinder walls and piston rings. The piston rings will then allow combustion leaks into the crankcase and oil into the cylinder. Many small engine mechanics do not use spark plug cleaning machines because of this danger. The aluminum cylinder walls in small engines are easily damaged. A new spark plug is quicker and may be much less expensive.

Spark plug cleaning machine

WOBBLE THE SPARK PLUG ABOUT SLOWLY WHILE ABRASIVE IS CLEANING IT

Cleaning a spark plug

4. File the electrode surfaces until they are flat and parallel. Thin ignition files are used for this job.

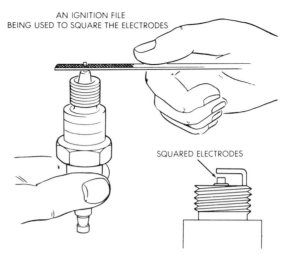

Squaring electrodes

Be careful: Use a spark plug socket wrench to remove or install spark plugs. They have special rubber liners that help to prevent damaging the ceramic insulator.

5. Adjust the spark gap by bending the side electrode with the gap gauge tool until the correct size gauge just fits between the electrodes with a gentle push.

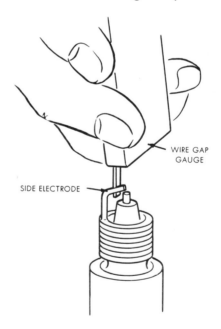

Be careful: Never try to bend the centre electrode. The insulator will break like glass.

Adjusting the spark plug gap by bending the side electrode

6. Install a new gasket and screw the spark plug into the cylinder head finger tight. With a wrench, tighten the plug just one half to three-quarters of a turn. The engine manual may suggest using a torque wrench for a more accurate job.

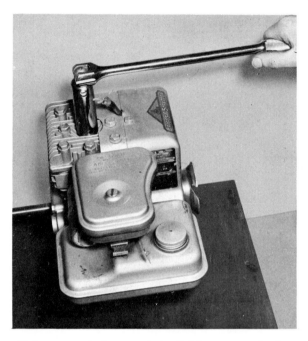

Using a socket wrench to tighten a spark plug

SPARK PLUG HEAT RANGES

Ordinarily it is a good idea to use the size and type of spark plug the engine maker recommends. However, if the recommended plug shows signs of being burned or is badly fouled after a short time of normal use, it may be operating *too hot* or *too cold.*

   The spark plug electrodes must work in the terrific heat of combustion. This heat must be taken away by the engine cooling system, or the electrodes will be burned off. The operating temperature or heat range of the electrodes depends on the distance from the spark plug's inside sealing gasket to the tip of its ceramic insulator.

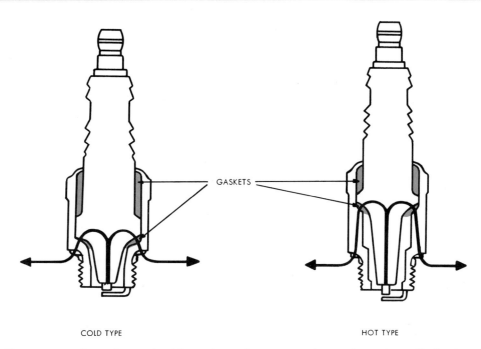

GASKETS

COLD TYPE

HOT TYPE

The arrows show the path of heat from the centre electrode to the cylinder head.

Spark plugs should operate at a temperature that is just hot enough to keep the electrodes and insulator clean by burning off any carbon deposits. A cold type spark plug has a short insulator tip that allows heat to escape quickly. It would be used for heavy duty and high speed operation to avoid overheating. The hot type plug has a long insulator tip. The long tip forces the heat to travel farther and take a longer time to escape. This causes the electrodes to run hot, so this type of plug is good for low speed operation to burn off combustion deposits.

SPARK PLUG SIZE

The size of a spark plug is named for the diameter and length of the threaded part of its shell. Most small engines use spark plugs with a 14 mm thread diameter. The 10 mm, 12 mm and 18 mm sizes are used by some manufacturers. Be careful to install a spark plug that has the correct thread length, or "reach." The spark plug must be able to reach the correct distance into the cylinder head to hold the electrodes in the best possible position for igniting the fuel. A spark plug with a reach that is too short will tend to carbon up quickly because the electrodes are sheltered and run too cool. A spark plug with a reach that is too long might contact the piston. The piston could then be damaged, or it could close up the spark gap by pushing the electrodes together. The centre electrode might be pushed up through its insulator. The electrodes could also run too hot and burn off.

Always use the size of spark plug described in the manufacturer's repair or owner's manual.

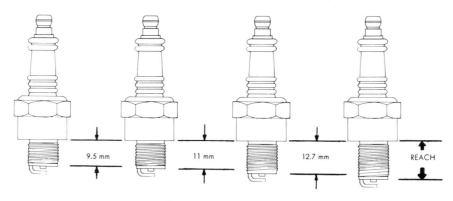

Spark plug reach

Timing the Spark

Find the Answers to These Questions

1. When is the best time for the spark plug to fire?
2. What parts of magnetos may be adjusted to time the spark?
3. What effect would late spark timing have on engine operation?
4. Where are timing marks usually found on a small engine?

You would think that the ideal time for the spark plug to fire would be when the piston is at the very top of the compression stroke and beginning to move down on the power stroke. However, if you think of the terrific speed of the piston in its cylinder, and the time it must take for all the fuel to burst into flame, you will see that the spark should jump across the spark

Safety Note: On some hand starters, kick-back can cause injury to fingers and hands. If there is any sign of kick-back, check the ignition timing.

plug electrodes just before the top of the compression stroke. Then all of the power in the fuel will be ready to push the piston down. Some time must be allowed for the fuel to begin burning.

The mass and speed of the flywheel keep the piston moving up against the force of the burning fuel. If the spark has been timed exactly right, nearly all of the fuel will be burning when the piston reaches the top of its travel. The pressure in the cylinder will be terrific, and the piston will be pushed down with all the power the fuel can deliver.

An engine that is timed too early will tend to kick backward when you try to start it. Late timing reduces engine power, and wastes fuel.

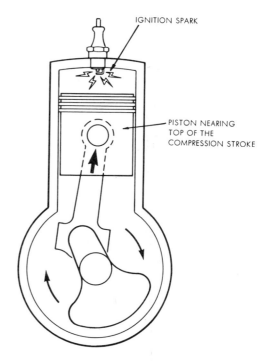

Spark timing

Some small engines have this spark timing designed into them and only the breaker point gap can be adjusted by a mechanic. Many more have a means of changing the timing by moving the magneto mounting plate to the best operating position. This may be a screw-tightened collar or slotted mounting holes in the mounting plate.

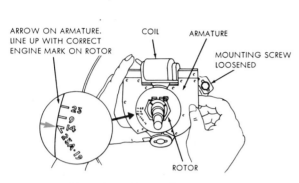

ARROW ON ARMATURE.
LINE UP WITH CORRECT
ENGINE MARK ON ROTOR   COIL   ARMATURE

MOUNTING SCREW
LOOSENED

ROTOR

Mounting plate adjustment

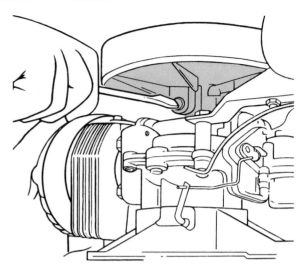

Magneto mounting plate adjustment

Some engine designs allow the spark timing to be adjusted while the engine is running. The mechanic may either listen to the engine or use a special timing light to find the best adjustment.

When a timing light is used, the mechanic adjusts the spark timing until a timing mark on the flywheel lines up with a mark on the magneto plate or cylinder block just as the light flashes. If the light is aimed at the timing marks, they will appear to stand still one above the other.

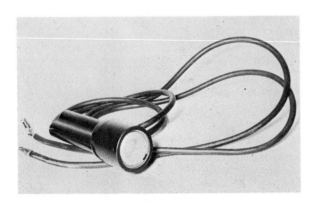

Timing light

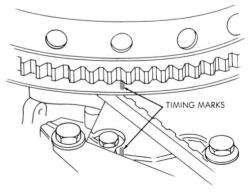

TIMING MARKS

Timing marks

Be careful: A timing problem may be caused by a partly-sheared key that has allowed the flywheel to turn out of position.

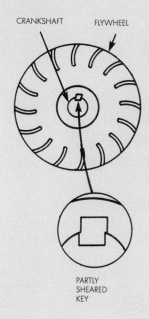

CRANKSHAFT   FLYWHEEL

PARTLY
SHEARED
KEY

Timing lights may also be used when the engine is not running. Some manufacturers make a special timing fixture for the engines they build. On these engines, the flywheel must be removed to install the timing fixture. The timing light is then connected across the breaker points. Turn the crankshaft slowly by hand. The timing light will indicate when the points open. At this instant, the timing fixture should be correctly lined up with the timing mark on the magneto plate. A small adjustment of the breaker points may be needed.

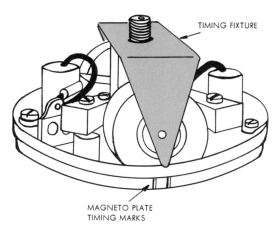

TIMING FIXTURE

MAGNETO PLATE
TIMING MARKS

A special fixture being used to time ignition

Often, the only timing adjustment that can be made is to adjust the breaker point gap. A wide gap will cause an early or advanced spark. A narrow gap will cause a late or retarded spark. This is why it is important to adjust the breaker points very carefully.

Many of the newest small engines have an electronic ignition system. This system uses diodes and transistors in a circuit. The transistors take the place of the breaker points and the diodes change the alternating current from the primary coil winding to direct current. The spark timing is controlled by the position of the magnet in the flywheel or the rotor in relation to the coil in the electronic unit. On some of these engines, the position of the electronic unit is adjusted for spark timing. On other engines no timing adjustment is needed. When adjusting the spark timing of any engine, the method described by the manufacturer is always the best method.

Flywheel Magneto Operation

Find the Answers to These Questions

1. Should the breaker points be closed or open as the magnet begins to pass the ignition coil?
2. What causes the sudden high voltage in the secondary coil?
3. Name two styles of electronic ignition systems.
4. How does an electronic circuit tend to improve the magneto ignition system?
5. What mechanical parts of the ordinary magneto are not needed in the electronic type of magneto?
6. What method is used to find out whether the magneto is working?

ELECTRO-MECHANICAL FLYWHEEL MAGNETO IGNITION

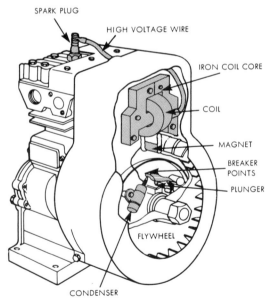

A cutaway drawing of a flywheel magneto

The next drawing shows a flywheel magneto with the coil, condenser, and breaker points in position. The permanent magnet is built into the flywheel, which is turning clockwise.

The magnet reaches a position with the North pole over the

Be careful: Be sure the ignition switch is turned off when working on machines powered by small engines.

centre of the coil. The magnetic field follows the iron core downward through the coil to the South pole. The breaker points are closed.

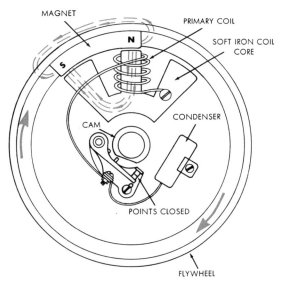

Magnetic lines of force passing through the iron coil core

As the flywheel continues to turn, the magnet moves so that the South pole begins to come into position over the centre of the coil. This suddenly reverses the magnetic field through the coil, causing a current to flow in the primary coil. This in turn causes a magnetic field to build up around the primary coil, passing through the secondary coil.

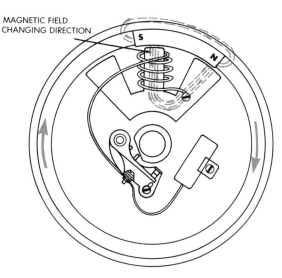

Magnetic field reversed

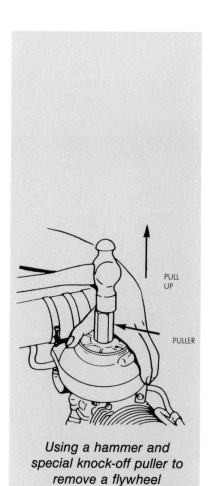

Using a hammer and special knock-off puller to remove a flywheel

When the magnet reaches the position shown below, the breaker points snap open. The current in the primary coil stops, and its magnetic field suddenly collapses. This rapid change in the magnetic field causes a great voltage in the secondary coil. This voltage forces a spark across the spark plug gap.

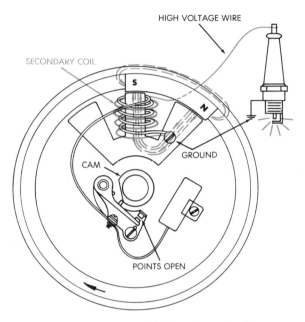

Breaker points snap open. High voltage in the secondary circuit produces an ignition spark.

ELECTRONIC MAGNETO IGNITION

Transistor: a small electronic device used to control an electrical current.

Diode: a diode is used to change alternating current to direct current. It is also called a rectifier.

Most electronic ignition systems used on small engines are magneto systems. One or more of the standard magneto parts is replaced with electronic circuits using transistors called diodes and silicon controlled rectifiers. Diodes allow electricity to pass in only one direction. They may be used to change alternating current to direct current. The electronic symbol for a diode looks like an arrow pointing at a wall and shows that electricity cannot flow in that direction.

The symbol for a diode

Silicon controlled rectifiers are often called gate controlled switches. Like a diode, an SCR will allow electricity to pass in one direction, but only when a second, small, positive trigger current opens its gate. Its symbol shows this third gate connection.

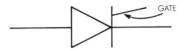

The symbol for a silicon controlled rectifier

In the drawings that follow, these symbols are used rather than views of the actual device. Since diodes and SCRs are easily damaged by water, the manufacturers seal the electronic circuitry in a plastic case. Often the ignition coils and condenser are sealed in the same case. On some engines, only the ignition switch can be damaged by water or worn out from use. The only adjustment may be the air gap between the flywheel and coil core.

When checking any magneto ignition system to find out if it is working, remove the spark plug, attach the high voltage lead

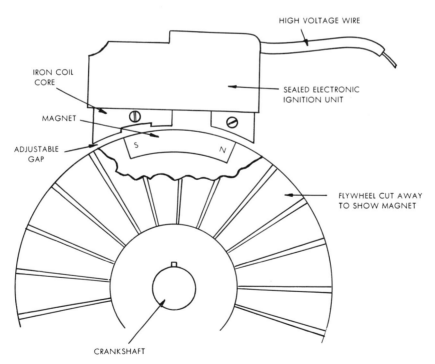

An electronic flywheel magneto

to it and ground its shell to the engine. Spin the flywheel and watch for a bright spark across the spark plug gap.

Transistors can become faulty, so it is possible that the electronic circuits may break down. There is no repair for this condition. The complete electronic ignition unit must be replaced.

Electronic Breakerless Ignition

This ignition system is like the ordinary magneto but there are no breaker points. The points are replaced by a silicon controlled rectifier and a diode. A small trigger coil and magnet produce the current needed to switch on the SCR.

The first drawing shows the flywheel turning and the lines of force from the magnet are pushing through the coil and producing a negative surge of current in the primary winding. The diode acts like closed breaker points and allows the current to flow to ground.

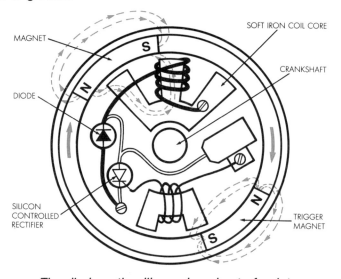

The diode acting like a closed set of points

As the flywheel continues to turn, the magnetic lines of force suddenly change direction through the coil and strong positive voltage is induced in the primary winding. The diode stops conducting at this same time; lines of force from the trigger coil magnet have pushed through the trigger coil and produced a positive charge in the lead to the gate of the SCR. This turns on the SCR which then takes over the passing of the current in the primary coil winding. The system still acts as it would with closed breaker points. A strong magnetic field builds up around the ignition coil.

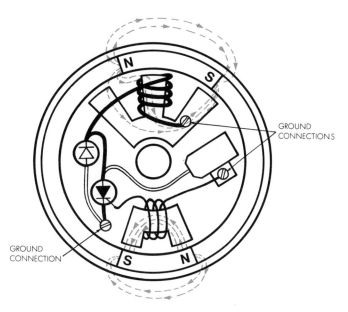

GROUND
CONNECTIONS

GROUND
CONNECTION

The magnetic field through the ignition coil reverses.
A positive charge on its gate turns on the SCR.

When the flywheel reaches the position shown in the last drawing, the strength of the magnetic field through the ignition coil is at its greatest. At this same time the motion of the trigger coil magnet is pulling lines of force away from the trigger coil winding, which causes a negative charge in the coil lead to the SCR. This turns off the SCR; the current in the primary ignition coil is stopped instantly by the condenser and the strong magnetic field through the coil collapses. This sudden collapse of the magnetic field causes a great voltage in the secondary winding which forces a spark across the spark plug gap.

Notice that in the illustrations, the parts of the system shown have not been drawn to scale. For example, the trigger coil and its magnet would be much smaller than the ignition coil and magnet in an actual magneto.

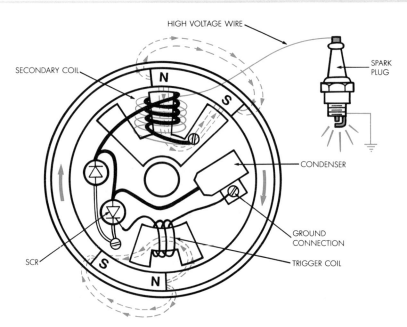

*The SCR stops conducting. High voltage in the secondary winding
of the ignition coil jumps across the spark plug gap.*

Capacitor Discharge Ignition

Capacitor: another name for a condenser.

The capacitor discharge ignition system is the most common electronic system used on small engines. There are many different arrangements of the parts and wiring used, but they all work in much the same way. Notice that the capacitor in this type of ignition system is much larger than the condenser described in other systems. This is because the capacitor must store enough electrical energy to build a strong magnetic field around the primary ignition coil at the correct time for fuel ignition.

The charging coil is wound on the centre leg of a three legged iron core and produces one complete cycle of alternating current as the flywheel magnet speeds past. To fully charge the capacitor, both halves of this cycle must be used, so four diodes are shown connected to form a full wave rectifier.

When the magnet moves past the charging coil, its lines of force first travel up through the coil and produce the first half of the alternating current cycle. This current is passed from the coil, through the rectifier to the storage capacitor.

Almost instantly, the magnetic lines of force through the coil change direction, and so does the electrical current in the coil. This is the second half of the alternating current cycle but the

Be careful: When an engine is running, you can get a strong electrical shock when handling high voltage parts like coils, capacitors, spark plugs and lead wires.

rectifier passes it in the same direction to the capacitor as before. Now the capacitor is fully charged.

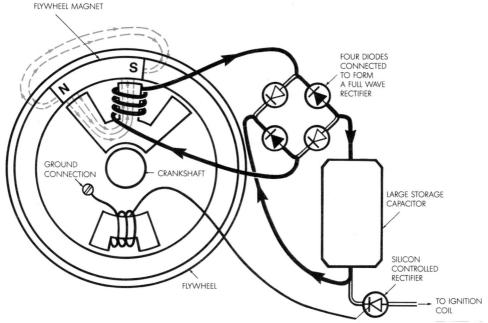

The storage capacitor being charged during the first half of the alternating current cycle.

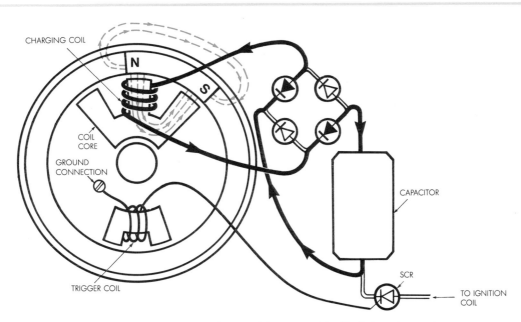

The storage capacitor being charged during the second half of the alternating current cycle.

The position of the trigger coil controls the ignition timing in this system. When the flywheel magnet reaches the position shown, its lines of force passing through the trigger coil produce a small positive current in the lead to the gate of the silicon controlled rectifier. This turns on the SCR and allows the electrical charge in the capacitor to unload through the primary ignition coil winding to ground. As the current rushes through the primary coil a very strong magnetic field builds up around it and produces the voltage needed in the secondary coil winding to force the current across the spark plug gap and ignite the fuel/air mixture.

You will notice that this is the only ignition system that produces its spark from energy created during a build-up of a magnetic field in the ignition coil instead of during a rapid collapse. This is made possible by the great speed of the current as it unloads from the storage capacitor.

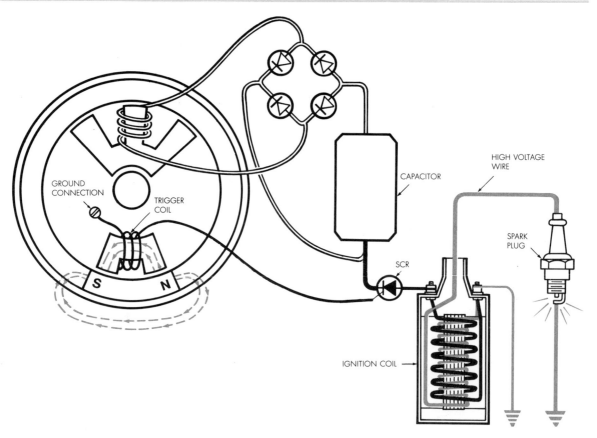

Current generated in the trigger coil turns on the SCR allowing the storage capacitor to unload through the primary circuit of the ignition coil.

Things to Do

1. Find examples of each of the styles of magnetos mentioned in this chapter. Examine their differences.

2. Examine a flywheel magneto and locate the parts and wire leads that make up the primary and secondary circuits.

3. Set up and try the iron filings experiment to show lines of force around a bar magnet.

4. Check the strength of a used flywheel magnet by comparing it to a new one.

5. Adjust the breaker points on a small engine magneto to the correct gap, as described in this chapter.

6. Remove, clean, and regap a spark plug, as described in this chapter.

7. Find examples of spark plugs with differing heat ranges.

8. Adjust the air gap between an ignition coil core and the flywheel. Follow the manufacturer's directions.

9. Check an electronic ignition system to see if it is producing spark.

CHAPTER 10

STORAGE AND TROUBLE SHOOTING

Preparing an Engine for Storage

Since most small engines are used during the warmer months of the year and then stored during the cold weather, it is good to know how to store an engine for the winter and how to get it ready for use again in the spring.

When storing an engine you will sometimes find that it is in need of repair or replacement of parts. If so, it is a good time to do the job.

1. Drain the fuel tank and the carburetor. If the carburetor cannot be drained, start the engine and run it until all fuel in the bowl is used up and the engine stops.

Be careful: Gasoline fumes are explosive. Do not drain fuel in a closed workshop or while smoking.

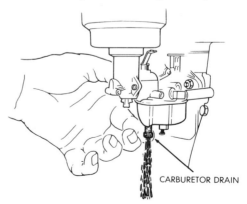

CARBURETOR DRAIN

DRAIN ALL GASOLINE

Drain the carburetor.

164

2. Change the crankcase oil for a four stroke cycle engine.
3. Remove the spark plug and squirt a small amount of lubricating oil through the spark plug hole to keep the upper cylinder from rusting. Replace the spark plug and turn the crankshaft several times to make sure that the oil is spread evenly over the cylinder walls.

Squirt lubricating oil into the cylinder.

4. Drain water from the cooling passages of outboard engines.
5. Add enough anti-freeze to engines with cooling radiators to prevent freezing, or drain the system.
6. Clean the exterior of the engine and cover it with a dust-proof wrapping. This could be a small garbage bag, a sheet of plastic or a piece of heavy cloth or paper.
7. Store the engine in a dry place.

Preparing an Engine for Use

1. Take the engine from storage and remove the dustproof wrappings.
2. Check the oil level if it is a four stroke cycle engine.

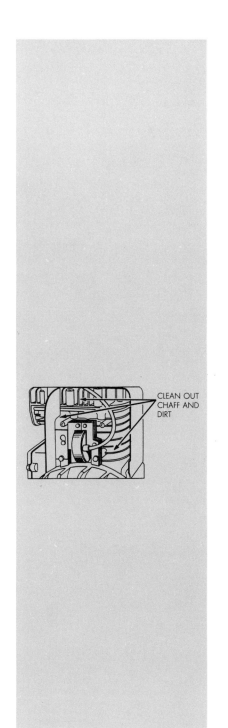

CLEAN OUT CHAFF AND DIRT

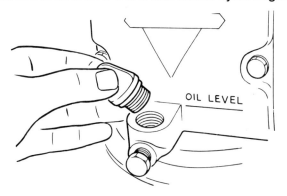

OIL LEVEL

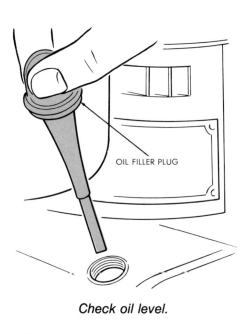

Check oil level.

3. Clean and regap or replace the spark plug if necessary.

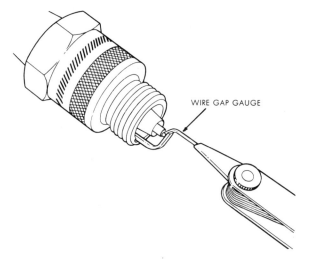

Check spark plug gap.

4. Clean the air cleaner element and bowl. Oil bath air cleaners will need to have fresh oil up to the oil level mark on the bowl.

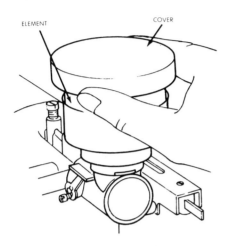
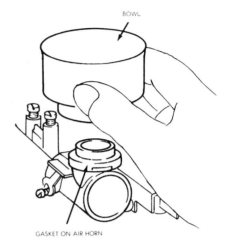

Remove the air cleaner for cleaning.

This is a good time to replace the element in dry element air cleaners.

5. Clean the fuel tank, fuel line and filter screen.
6. Fill the fuel tank with clean fresh fuel.

Be careful: When using a funnel be sure it is made of metal to ground the spout to the tank.

Use funnel to avoid spilling fuel on engine.

7. Fill the cooling system of water-cooled engines with clean, fresh water and add anti-freeze or a rust inhibitor.
8. Start the engine and adjust the carburetor for smooth running at all speeds.

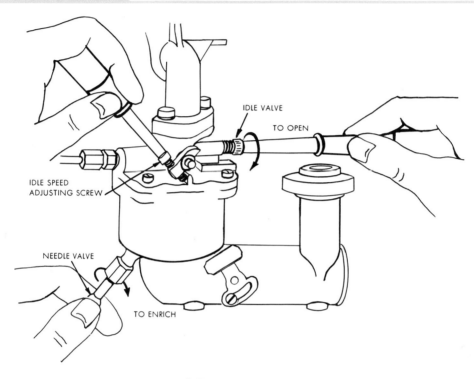

Adjust carburetor.

Trouble-Shooting an Engine

ENGINE FAILS TO START OR IS HARD TO START

Cause	Correction
1. No fuel in the tank.	Fill the tank with clean, fresh fuel.
2. Fuel shut-off valve closed.	Open the shut-off valve.
3. Fuel line plugged or kinked.	Clean or replace fuel line.
4. Suction tube screen plugged. Ball stuck.	Clean screen. Replace tube if ball is stuck.
5. Water in the fuel.	Drain and clean the fuel tank. Refill with clean, fresh fuel.
6. Stale fuel in the tank.	Drain and clean the fuel tank. Refill with clean, fresh fuel.
7. Weak or no high voltage at the spark plug.	Check the breaker points, coil, condenser, high tension lead and magnet strength. Adjust or replace as needed.
8. Spark will not jump spark gap.	Check condition of spark plug. Replace if cleaning and gapping fail to correct trouble.
9. Ignition switch in off position.	Move switch to on position.

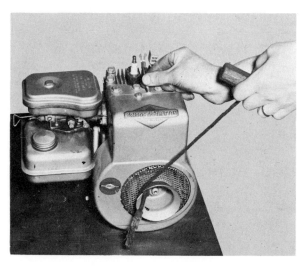

Weak or no high voltage at the spark plug

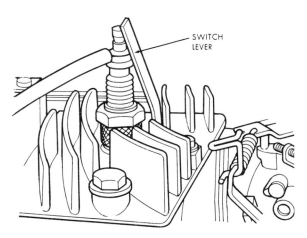

Ignition switch off

Cause	**Correction**
10. Engine flooded with fuel.	Open the choke and close the fuel tank valve. Crank engine until excess fuel is forced out exhaust.
11. Choke partly open.	Close the choke completely. Adjust choke cable.

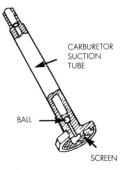

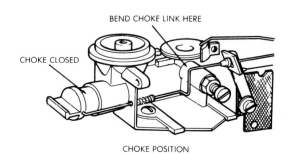

Clean the screen and check the looseness of the ball.

Adjust choke cable.

12. Carburetor needs adjustment.	Adjust needle valve and idle mixture to the recommended settings.
13. Throttle closed.	Open throttle to fast or run position. Check for binding linkage or unhooked governor linkage.
14. Plugged exhaust ports, two stroke engine.	Remove muffler and clean the ports.

Clean the carbon from plugged exhaust ports. Be careful to have the piston skirt covering the ports so carbon chunks cannot fall into the cylinder. Do not scratch the piston.

Cause	Correction
15. Bent or broken reed valve, two stroke engine.	Replace the reed or reed valve assembly.

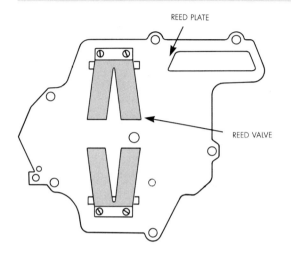

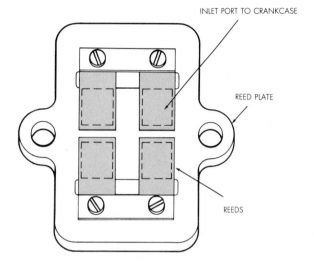

A REED VALVE PLATE WITH TWO REED VALVES AS USED ON TWO CYLINDER OUTBOARD ENGINES

If reeds are bent or broken, replace them.

Cause	Correction
16. Leaking oil seals or gaskets, two stroke engine.	Install new oil seal or gasket set.
17. Low or no compression. Caused by:	
(a) blown head gasket;	Replace gasket and torque head bolts to specifications.
(b) worn or broken piston rings;	Remove piston, clean, replace rings.
(c) valves not seating tightly; valves sticking, burned or warped; worn valve seats.	Remove defective valve or seat. Recondition or replace as needed.

If compression improves when oil is squirted around the piston rings, valve seats are good and piston rings need replacement.

Cause	Correction

18. Carburetor or fuel tank vent blocked with dirt.

Clean out vent holes.

ENGINE MISFIRING UNDER LOAD

Cause	Correction

1. Weak or irregular spark.

Check the points, condenser, coil leads, coil and magnet strength.

2. Worn or fouled spark plug.

Replace with new spark plug.

3. Air cleaner plugged or choke partly closed.

Service the air cleaner or open the choke, whichever is needed.

4. Carburetor needs adjustment, mixture too lean.

Adjust the needle valve to give a richer mixture.

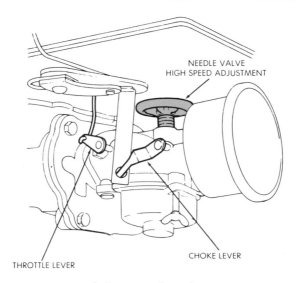

NEEDLE VALVE
HIGH SPEED ADJUSTMENT

CHOKE LEVER

THROTTLE LEVER

Adjust needle valve.

5. Float bowl or fuel tank vent blocked with dirt.

Clean out vent holes.

Cause	Correction
6. Fuel not reaching carburetor.	Remove and clean the fuel tank. Clean or replace fuel line and filter screen.

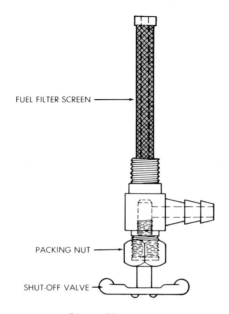

FUEL FILTER SCREEN

PACKING NUT

SHUT-OFF VALVE

Clean filter screen.

7. Ignition shut-off not in the full *on* position.	Move or adjust shut-off to full *on* position.
8. Engine running too hot.	Cooling system should be cleaned. Clean or repair water intake and pump, on water cooled engines. Check oil level. Drain and refill if needed
9. Too much or too little oil mixed with gasoline, two cycle engine.	Drain the fuel tank and refill with correct fuel mix.
10. Plugged exhaust system.	Clean exhaust ports (two stroke). Remove, clean or replace muffler.

Cause	**Correction**
11. Low compression.	Recondition or replace valves and valve seats. Replace worn piston rings.

Compression gauge

Pull starter rope firmly. Compare the compression reading on the gauge with the manufacturer's specifications.

12. Weak valve springs.	Install new valve springs.

When weak valve spring is compared to new valve spring, the used one will be seen to be shorter.

Cause	Correction
13. Reed valve bent, two stroke engine.	Replace the reed or the reed valve assembly.
14. Crankcase seals or gaskets leaking, two stroke engine.	Replace the faulty seals or gaskets.

ENGINE SURGES, WILL NOT HOLD STEADY SPEED

Cause	Correction
1. Float bowl or fuel tank vents are plugged.	Clean out vent holes.
2. Float level set too low.	Adjust the float to correct level.

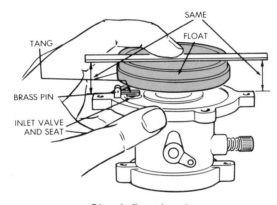

Check float level.

Cause	Correction
3. Fuel tank screen or fuel line partly plugged.	Clean the tank, screen, fuel line, and float needle and seat.

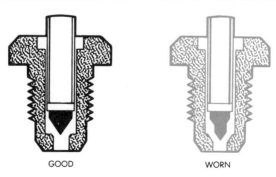

Replace worn needle and seat.

Cause	**Correction**
4. Needle valve out of adjustment.	Adjust the needle valve.
5. Governor, linkage binding.	Clean and repair or replace the governor parts.
6. Throttle or throttle shaft binding.	Clean and deburr the throttle and shaft.
7. Throttle or governor springs unhooked, broken or in wrong position.	Connect or replace the spring in the correct position.

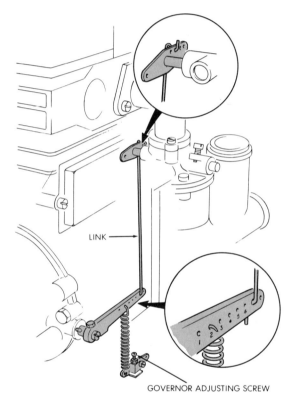

LINK

GOVERNOR ADJUSTING SCREW

Check the governor spring and link position, using the engine manual.

ENGINE RATTLES OR KNOCKS

Cause	**Correction**
1. Piston hitting carbon deposit in upper cylinder.	Remove cylinder head or pot and clean out all carbon.
2. Loose blade, pulley, gear or clutch on end of crankshaft.	Tighten or replace the loose part.
3. Loose connecting rod cap.	Tighten connecting rod bolts and bend up locking lugs.

Cause	**Correction**
4. Worn connecting rod or crankshaft.	Replace the connecting rod and/or the crank-shaft.
5. Worn main bearings, see (A), (B) and (C), below.	Replace the bearings and the crankshaft if necessary.
6. Loose flywheel.	Replace flywheel key and tighten the flywheel to the correct torque.

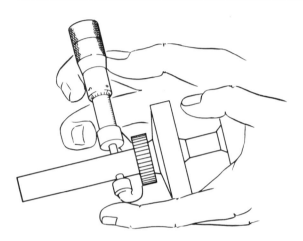

A Measure the amount of wear on a bearing surface using a micrometer.

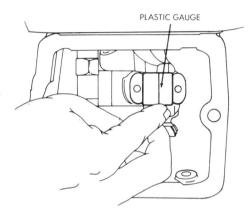

B Check bearing wear with a special plastic gauge. Place a strip of gauge material between the crankshaft and the bearing cap. With the bearing cap in position tighten the cap screws firmly.

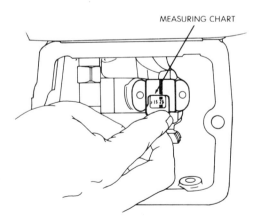

C Remove the bearing cap and compare the width of the crushed gauge material to a chart. The chart will show the bearing clearance in fractions of a millimetre or of an inch.

ENGINE HAS TOO MUCH VIBRATION

Cause	Correction
1. Blade, pulley, gear or clutch out of balance.	Balance or replace out of balance part.
2. Engine loose on its mounting.	Tighten the mounting bolts.
3. Bent crankshaft.	Install a new crankshaft.
4. Flywheel fan blades broken off.	Replace the flywheel with a new one.

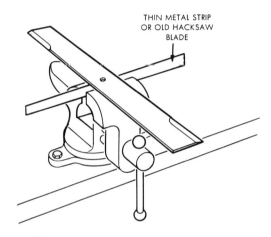

THIN METAL STRIP OR OLD HACKSAW BLADE

Check the balance of mower blade.

ENGINE RUNS TOO HOT

Cause	Correction
1. Oil level low in crankcase.	Drain the crankcase and refill with oil of the correct viscosity.
2. Not enough oil in the fuel, two stroke engine.	Drain the fuel tank and refill with the correct fuel and oil mix.
3. Air cooling fins blocked with dirt.	Clean out the areas between the cooling fins.
4. Shroud not in place or screen is plugged.	Clean and replace the shroud.
5. Water pump worn or passages plugged.	Repair or replace water pump. Clean the cooling passages.

Cause	Correction
6. Carburetor set too lean.	Adjust needle valve to give a richer fuel/air mixture.
7. Ignition system out of time.	Retime the ignition to the correct firing point.

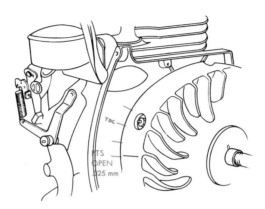

Timing the ignition

Things to Do

1. Locate a small engine owner's manual and read the section on engine servicing and maintenance.
2. Prepare a small engine for winter storage.
3. Prepare a small engine for use after storage.
4. Use the troubleshooting chart while checking a small engine.

A small garden tiller

Index